A PARROT'S
HEALTHY DINING
Go Raw!

A PARROT'S HEALTHY DINING

Go Raw!

Avian Nutritional Guide and Recipes for all Species

KARMEN BUDAI

Polly's
Natural Parrot Boutique

For permissions contact:
info@pollysnaturalparrotboutique.com
www.pollysnaturalparrotboutique.com

Publisher: K&S Natural Company Ltd, 71–75 Shelton Street, Covent Garden, London WC2H 9JQ, United Kingdom

Text copyright © 2020 Karmen Budai, K&S Natural Company Ltd
Article contributors: Dr Karen Becker, DVM; Dr Stephanie Lamb, DVM; Dr Jamie Abete, DVM
Cover, layout and design by Goldust Design
Food photography by Karmen Budai
Editor: Wendy Janes

ISBN 978-1-5272-7633-8

CONTENTS

FOREWORD

A well-balanced diet is as important for our pets as for us humans. What you feed your pet bird will have a big impact on their health and overall wellbeing during their life. Therefore introducing the right diet from the start when your bird is still young will ensure they get all the nutrients needed for growth, prevent diet-related illnesses and help form good eating habits too. Feeding your bird, a fresh raw whole food diet will require your full commitment as fresh food is not something that comes as a ready meal that can go straight into a parrot's bowl. There is more to it and it will take time, preparation and patience in order to give nutritionally balanced meals without needing to supplement them with any processed foods.

In my first book I tried to cover the basics when it comes to avian nutrition, with fantastic articles from the best avian experts out there, helping you understand what is really needed in order to maintain your bird's healthy lifestyle by offering the right foods.

In this book I will continue and expand on a variety of interesting topics concerning avian nutrition and the latest recommendations from the avian veterinarians, complemented with over 30 healthy recipes catering for all species from small to large beaks.

Karmen Budai and Polly

Preparing, deliciously healthy foods for your bird has never been easier!

Nutritional Guide

WHY PET BIRDS NEED SPECIES-APPROPRIATE FRESH FOOD DIETS

by Dr Karen Shaw Becker, DVM

Story At-A-Glance

❯ Decades ago, it was common for avian veterinarians to recommend fortified seed diets as the gold standard for pet birds, followed by the trend of only feeding fortified pellets (similar to dry pet food) to meet minimum nutritional requirements.

❯ Now it's known that seed-based diets and one-size-fits-all pellets are lacking in important aspects of species-specific bird nutrition and may lead to nutritional diseases such as obesity, reproductive disorders, abnormal feathers and organ dysfunction.

❯ The best diets for exotic birds are diets that most closely mimic a bird's native diet and include an abundance of fresh, live, whole foods, which provide natural foraging opportunities and vitamins and minerals from bioavailable sources.

❯ More and more avian veterinarians are recognizing the important role of species-appropriate nutrition for the birds they keep and are seeing improved health and vitality as a result, making excellent nutrition a priority.

If you're new to sharing your life with a pet bird, you may assume that they eat mostly seeds or pellets. This, however, is setting her up for probable nutritional disease and eventual organ degeneration, which can occur over time due to dietary deficiencies or excesses.

Decades ago, it was common for veterinarians to recommend fortified seed diets or extruded pellets (aka "bird kibble") as the gold standard for pet bird nutrition. Many pet birds were also fed poor-quality sunflower and peanut mixes, which are too high in fat and deficient in antioxidants, phytonutrients, vitamins and minerals, which contributed to the vast majority of captive birds dying notably early deaths.

Avian veterinarians now know there's no one-size-fits-all diet that's good for all birds, as each species has different nutritional requirements. Macaws, for instance, need a higher fat content in their food while cockatoos do better with lower fat and higher protein. Knowing your pet bird's nutritional requirements, as a species, is crucial in ensuring she stays disease-free and healthy.

Photo by Christopher Alvarenga

Birds Do Best Eating Their Natural Diet

We've learned, the hard way, that taking a one-size-fits-all approach to exotic bird nutrition is a bad idea. Many seed-addicted parrots don't live to see half of their expected lifespan, and while there are many factors that contribute to a parrot's healthspan, the role of species-appropriate nutrition is a critical piece of the psittacine longevity equation.

In the 90s, avian vets (including myself) assumed "nutritionally complete and balanced" extruded pellets ("bird food") would dramatically improve the nutritional status of our malnourished avian patients.

This novel approach for birds resulted in the same issues we see with our dog and cat patients eating a lifetime of kibble: animals with weight issues, skin problems, an increase in behaviour problems and a wad of chronic, degenerative diseases not seen in their wild counterparts.

Birds are highly sensitive animals — much more so than dogs and cats. Ninety-nine percent of mass-produced bird foods on the market are made with non-inspected "feed grade" ingredients, so the levels of heavy metals, mycotoxins, pesticide residues and contaminants can be profound.

Add to that, synthetic dyes, preservatives, emulsifiers and a slew of synthetic vitamins and minerals (coming from China), not to mention the by-products of processing itself, and it's easy to see why many avian vets (including myself) hopped off the pellet bandwagon a while ago. Thankfully we've learned a lot over the last 20 years.

Photo by Akshay Madan

Transitioning Your Bird to a Healthier Diet

Not unlike finicky felines, many birds are addicted to their poor quality diets and must be transitioned slowly, with tremendous patience and maybe some trickery, to begin exploring healthier food choices.

I suggest considering how the bird species you keep lives its life in the wild. Offering foods like shredded vegetables and sprouted seeds on the cage floor for foraging is species-appropriate for birds like cockatiels, while hanging foods from stainless steel skewers in larger chunks could be a great method of engaged eating for a macaw.

Offering whole foods diced, shredded, in chunks or whole and considering how and where you present them could be the gateway to better eating.

How you present foods to your birds may be critical to them actually recognizing new items as a food. It can take days, weeks, months, or longer, but never stop trying different ways for your birds to eat better foods. More often than not, you cannot offer a food once or twice and claim that your bird doesn't like it; persistence on your part is key!

Why Foraging Matters to the Food Experience

One of the most underestimated aspects of avian wellness that has become very apparent in the last decade is environmental enrichment, including food foraging experiences.

Knowing how birds behave and not expecting human-like behaviours from them helps a great deal when you consider their preferences for foraging. Providing species-appropriate foraging involves allowing them to work for their food, which research shows animals prefer.

Foraging could mean birds need to move things around in order to get to foods, or open something to access some foods. It isn't uncommon for birds to hang upside down just to reach their favourite food item.

Mixing foods together can help them forage, and it's also a great way to introduce new foods. Making a mash that consists of soaked and sprouted seeds and grains, diced and shredded vegetables, fresh or dried edible flowers, and even some fruit can be a great way to start. Birds try new food items they have never encountered before when mixed into a mash.

As more and more people see their birds as integral members of their families, they are recognizing the important roles of species-appropriate avian nutrition and foraging experiences in their birds' overall health. Feeding a diverse whole food diet rich in unprocessed foods can take your bird from just surviving to thriving.

Thankfully, there are a variety of educational groups and websites to help you become a well-informed and knowledgeable avian owner.

Reprinted with permission

Source: Mercola.com

MYTHS ABOUT RAW FOOD OR WHY VETS DON'T RECOMMEND RAW FOODS

By Dr Jamie Abete, DVM

Opinions on how to feed parrots are varied and have evolved over time with our increasing knowledge of how to care for our avian companions. The invention of a pelleted parrot diet in the 1970s changed the way we think about feeding birds – now there was a "complete" diet we could offer all species of birds similar to kibbled dog food. Pelleted diets were a breakthrough that improved the health of many birds that were mostly subsisting on all-seed diets, which are mostly fat and nutritionally inadequate as a complete diet. Typically whole raw food diets are not recommended due to the fear that they will be incomplete nutritionally and the pet bird's health will suffer. Absolutely a fresh food diet can be nutritionally devoid, but with a little effort it can be nutritionally superior to formulated diets.

One of the biggest myths about raw food diets is that they are ALWAYS nutrient deficient. Of course they can be – I have seen many avian patients that were being fed whatever the owners were eating or whatever fresh foods the owners typically ate themselves. Unfortunately many humans do not consume nutrient dense fresh foods and consider apples, pears, bananas, oranges and grapes to be adequate fresh food supplementation for their bird, with an occasional offering of broccoli or other green vegetables. Fresh whole food diets

Photo by Christopher Alvarenga

have amazing potential to be geared exactly towards the species of bird they are offered to, which is an extreme limitation with formulated diets that typically only come in a "one size fits all" formula. Another benefit of raw diets is that the vitamins and minerals in a raw diet are in their natural form, not added back in individually in a vitamin mixture after high heat processing denatured and destroyed the vitamins in the processed foods. Of course, cooking foods is not all bad, heating does make some foods more digestible, this, however, is typically not an issue for most pet birds as many are already overweight.

Another misconception I often hear about whole raw food diets for parrots is that they are unsafe to feed due to food spoilage concerns. There are plenty of ways to mitigate the concern of foods "going bad" during the day while the parrot owner is away at work – offering only the amount that will be eaten in three to four hours, adding in spices like oregano that inhibit microbial growth and offering foods that are cooler in temperature. Not offering quickly spoiling foods when you are going to be gone most of the day and limiting the amount of foods offered can go a long way. Birds in the wild are also often eating foods that are overripe, on the ground or even fermented, not all bacteria on foods are pathogenic. Contamination of food crops (like the recent E. coli contamination of spinach and romaine lettuce) is a bigger concern than food spoilage in a few hours. To save time in the morning, many owners feed foods that they store in the freezer, then defrost in the refrigerator overnight (or even a couple hours) before feeding – typically these foods are still quite cool when offered and take longer to get to room temperature which slows bacterial growth.

One of the main reasons why many veterinarians do not recommend a whole raw food diet is they are afraid it will be very unbalanced nutritionally and lead to other health problems. When offering a whole raw food diet you have to be committed to offering a large diversity of foods to meet your bird's nutritional requirements. You have to dedicate time for meal prepping for your bird to ensure you are offering a sufficient variety of vitamins, nutrients, carbohydrates, fats and proteins. There are plenty of ways to offer a complete fresh food diet, it just requires a bit of planning. Sometimes the best planning can go wrong too – some birds are quite resistant to new foods. If you have

a bird that has only gotten the occasional apple slice, taking away their normal diet and offering a chop mix tomorrow may not go well. When introducing your bird to a new diet you have to move slowly and monitor them to see what they are actually eating. Taking note of what foods are left in the bowl or thrown to the bottom of the cage every day will tell you a lot – if your bird is picking out all the fruits daily and not eating any greens you will need to change your feeding strategy to make sure the diet your bird is EATING is balanced.

Feeding a nutritionally balanced raw food diet can be very good for your parrot both physically and psychologically as it will offer an enriching variety that a formulated pellet cannot possibly provide. As with all diet changes, do not move too quickly and monitor your bird closely while switching. Ensuring that your bird gets a veterinarian check-up every year to make sure no evidence of any nutrient deficiencies are seen and offering a rotating schedule of different foods will likely ensure that you are safely supplying a complete diet. There are many reliable resources for appropriate parrot diet recipes that can be found in literature and online; as always, variety is key.

SPECIAL DIETARY NEEDS IN CERTAIN SPECIES

Macaws, Lorikeets and Lories, Eclectus

By Dr Jamie Abete, DVM

Macaws

Macaws are a diverse group of birds in both size and appearance.

One of the most striking aspects of a macaw's appearance besides its plumage is its rather large beak. As with most avian species, the size and shape of the beak tend to determine their dietary preferences. Macaws have a tremendous amount of beak strength that allows them to easily crack harder and larger nuts than most birds. In the wild, a macaw's diet consists of fruits, seeds, nuts and other plant parts. Wild macaws have been observed eating parts of over 40 different species of plants, suggesting they are adaptable in diet and enjoy substantial diversity in the foods they consume. [7]

Macaws are thought to have higher fat requirements than other species of parrots. A study that was carried out on wild macaws showed that they are consuming not only higher levels of fat, but also higher levels of calcium and magnesium than is currently recommended in formulated parrot diets, suggesting that a formulated diet alone may not meet a macaw's full nutritional needs.[2]

Foods that are high in protein and fat are thought to make up most of a wild macaw's diet, particularly while raising offspring.[3] Macaws are generally considered to be herbivores. There are some reports of macaws eating animal and insect proteins in the wild, but these observations have been refuted by later studies that focused specifically on wild macaw diets.[4] It is likely that captive macaws do not require as much dietary fat as wild macaws due to a relatively sedentary lifestyle when compared to their wild counterparts.

Macaws are considered to be especially prone to kidney damage when given a diet formulated or supplemented with more vitamin D than recommended.[6] Excessive vitamin D causes birds to absorb more calcium, which they then may deposit in the kidneys and other tissues, leading to kidney dysfunction and failure. Diets higher than 0.7% calcium have been implicated in causing kidney calcification.[1] The level of sodium found in wild macaw diets is much lower than the amount currently recommended in formulated diets, suggesting that macaws may have lower sodium requirements than other parrots.[2] More studies are needed to determine specific daily sodium requirements for macaws.

In captivity, macaws are very prone to respiratory and sinus issues, often at least in part caused by a lack of dietary vitamin A. Typically, birds not getting enough vitamin A will have lower respiratory immunity because vitamin A plays a major role in maintaining healthy mucous membranes. Hypovitaminosis A causes sneezing, inflammation of the mouth, blunted choanal papillae and excessive oral mucus.[5] Vitamin A deficiencies have also been shown to lead to kidney dysfunction, so it is especially important that macaws have a diet that is rich in natural sources of vitamin A, which includes a plethora of dark leafy greens and foods that are brightly coloured (generally foods that are orange in colour, except oranges) to protect them from easily avoidable medical problems.

Macaws are especially predisposed to developing goitre, which is an enlargement of the thyroid gland that occurs when the diet is deficient in iodine for an extended period of time.[1] Birds presenting with goitre typically have a change of voice and increased respiratory noise. This condition is most common in macaws fed an all-seed diet, but it can occur on any diet if the foods fed are cultivated in soil deficient in iodine. There are foods that are naturally rich in iodine like eggs, but the amounts of iodine in foods are not uniform across the globe due to varying amounts of iodine in the soil worldwide. Supplementation of iodine should only be done under the direct care of a veterinarian, as elevated levels of iodine can be quite harmful. Typically formulated pellet diets contain enough iodine to prevent the occurrence of goitre.[1]

Care must be taken to not oversupplement macaws with vitamin mixtures or provide an inadequate poorly varied or single-source diet (seeds, nuts). Supplementation of nutrients carries risk, especially for macaws. Addition of any vitamin or mineral supplement should only be done under the care of an avian veterinarian. The best way to ensure that your macaw thrives is to offer a varied diet high in nutrient dense plant foods that includes mostly green foods, antioxidant and vitamin rich fruits and healthy tree nuts.

Works Cited:

[1] Bandyopadhyay, Samiran. "Systemic Clinical and Metabolic Diseases." *Pet Bird Diseases and Care*, 2017, pp. 167–252., doi:10.1007/978-981-10-3674-3_3.

[2] Brightsmith, Donald J., et al. "Nutritional Content of the Diets of Free-Living Scarlet Macaw Chicks in Southeastern Peru." *Journal of Avian Medicine and Surgery*, vol. 24, no. 1, 2010, pp. 9–23., doi:10.1647/1082-6742-24.1.9.

[3] Contreras-González, A. M., et al. "Feeding Ecology of Military Macaws (Ara Militaris) in a Semi-Arid Region of Central México." *The Wilson Journal of Ornithology*, vol. 121, no. 2, 2009, pp. 384–391., doi:10.1676/08-034.1.

[4] Jordan, Rick, and Mark Moore. *A Guide to... Macaws as Pet & Aviary Birds*. ABK Publications, 2015.

[5] Sakas, Peter S., and Louise Bauck. *Essentials of Avian Medicine: a Guide for Practitioners*. American Animal Hospital Association Press, 2002.

[6] Schoemaker, N. J., et al. "Polyuria and Polydipsia Due to Vitamin and Mineral Oversupplementation of the Diet of a Salmon Crested Cockatoo (Cacatua Moluccensis) and a Blue and Gold Macaw (Ara Ararauna)." *Avian Pathology*, vol. 26, no. 1, 1997, pp. 201–209., doi:10.1080/03079459708419206.

[7] Vaughan, Christopher, et al. "Scarlet Macaw, Ara Macao, (Psittaciformes: Psittacidae) Diet in Central Pacific Costa Rica." *Revista De Biología Tropical*, vol. 54, no. 3, Sept. 2006., doi:10.15517/rbt.v54i3.13689.

Lorikeets and Lories

Lorikeets and lories are some of the most entertaining parrots to observe in both captivity and in the wild. As naturally gregarious, mischievous and noisy birds, their antics often captivate onlookers. The rainbow lorikeet is probably the most well-recognized member of the Loriinae family, but there are over 50 species of lory and lorikeet primarily from Australia, New Guinea and Indonesia.[3] Typically lories have rounder shorter tails, while lorikeets have longer tails. Lorikeet is often used as a "catch all" term for all members of the Loriinae family.

In the wild, lorikeets primarily eat the nectar and pollen of flowers as well as fruits. They have a highly specialized brush tongue that allows them to extract pollen and nectar from deep within flowers. They have also been occasionally seen eating insects as well as leaf buds. The most important component of the lorikeet diet in the wild appears to be eucalyptus flowers, so most captive diets are aimed at mimicking the sugar and nutrient concentrations found in these flowers. [1, 2, 4]

Dried nectar solutions that are reconstituted or offered dry, typically take up the bulk of most captive lorikeet diets. It is recommended that the sugar content of nectar substitutes offered should be between 25–30%.[4] When nectar substitutes are offered in higher sugar concentrations, they can pull more water from the bird's body into the digestive tract, causing dehydration, which can potentially lead to kidney dysfunction and gout.[4] Overly dilute sugar mixtures are very prone to spoilage and bacterial overgrowth. It is recommended to avoid diets that contain insoluble starches (like rice, wheat flour, other grains), as they tend to separate from the sugar and water portion, settling to the bottom of the container, which leads bacterial overgrowth.[4] Due to the high sugar content of lorikeet diets, an ample supply of fresh water should always be offered to prevent dehydration. A separate water bowl must always be available, as the nectar water mixture these birds consume does not provide adequate hydration.

In addition to a nectar substitute that makes up the majority of the lorikeet diet, these birds should be offered a wide variety of other fresh foods, including many dark leafy greens and fruits. Lorikeets are known to enjoy grapes, apples, mangos, berries and melons. They also will eat many vegetables, including broccoli, corn, leafy greens, etc. It is not recommended to offer lorikeets seeds or nuts – often they will eat these foods if provided, but they are not known to eat these foods in the wild and lack the beak density that seed eating birds have. Lorikeets have a much weaker gizzard (where seed is ground up prior to digestion) and shorter intestinal

Photo by Trevor Mckinnon

tract than other parrot species, which leaves them unable to properly digest seeds.[5] Sprouted seeds, however, are perfectly fine to feed in moderation and very much enjoyed by many lories. Lorikeets also enjoy edible flowers such as hibiscus.

Lorikeets are very prone to obesity in captivity. It is common for lorikeets to be offered an ad lib (as much as they can eat) diet of nectar, but this leads to them eating way more calories than a captive lorikeet can possibly use in a day. Overfeeding of nectar can also be dangerous, as it is prone to spoilage.[4] Nectar mixtures should be disposed of after a few hours to prevent harmful bacterial overgrowth. It is best to observe how much nectar mixture your bird typically consumes in a span of a few hours and only offer that amount of nectar with a variety of other healthy food options (fruits, vegetables, etc). Weighing your bird weekly and monitoring daily food consumption is the best way to determine if you are feeding your lorikeet an appropriate amount of food for their particular energy needs. If you are unsure if your bird is overweight or getting enough nutrients, consult with your avian veterinarian who will need to examine your bird at least yearly to give you good advice on health and nutrition. In addition to obesity, lorikeets are prone to getting gastrointestinal infections if their food is left out longer than it should be or if they are offered an inappropriate diet. Lorikeets typically have very wet droppings since they consume so much water in their diet and require frequent enclosure cleanings.

Works Cited:

[1] Cannon, Christine E. "The Diet of Lorikeets Trichoglossus Spp in the Queensland-New South Wales Border Region." *Emu - Austral Ornithology*, vol. 84, no. 1, 1984, pp. 16–22., doi:10.1071/mu9840016.

[2] Higgins, Peter Jeffrey. *Handbook of Australian, New Zealand & Antarctic Birds*. Oxford University Press, 1999.

[3] "Loriidae." *Parrots of the World*. Illustr. by William T. Cooper, by Joseph M. Forshaw, Doubleday, 1977, pp. 43–103.

[4] Rich, Gordon. "Optimum Sugar Concentration in Artificial Nectar Diets for Lorikeets." Association of Avian Veterinarians Australian Committee, LTD. , www.aavac.com.au, 2015, www.aavac.com.au/files/2015-07.pdf.

[5] Richardson, K.C., and R.D. Wooller. "Adaptations of the Alimentary Tracts of Some Australian Lorikeets to a Diet of Pollen and Nectar." *Australian Journal of Zoology*, vol. 38, no. 6, 1990, p. 581., doi:10.1071/zo9900581.

Eclectus

Eclectus parrots are one of the most unique species of parrot in their appearance, reproductive strategy and wild foraging practices. The male and female eclectus are so different in appearance that they were originally thought to be two separate species. Female eclectus are more colourful than the males in a striking example of reverse sexual dichromatism. Most parrot species tend to pair bond closely, often for life. Eclectus have an unconventional reproductive strategy when compared to other parrot species and tend to have multiple partners, practising cooperative breeding; a practice where more than two adults care for offspring in one nest. A single hen may have up to seven unrelated suitors that care for her while she is protecting her nest and offspring.[5] Eclectus were once considered to be the only species of cooperative breeding parrot, but it has since been observed in a few other species.[1,3,7] Eclectus parrots also have a remarkable level of control over determining what sex their offspring will be. Some hens have been reported to have up to 20 of the same-sex offspring in a row.[3] Eclectus hens have one of the most pronounced nest guarding instincts in the parrot family, protecting a suitable nest hollow for up to nine months at a time, relying entirely on her multiple male partners to provide for her and their offspring.[4]

It is not surprising that a parrot species with such an unusual reproductive strategy and remarkable physical appearance would have a somewhat different dietary approach than most parrots do. Eclectus are considered herbivores. In the wild, eclectus forage for food in the canopy of the forest rather than

Photo by Mehmet Turgut Kirkgoz

on the ground like many parrots do. They have been observed eating fruits, nuts, flowers, leaf buds and shoots as well as seeds.[2] There are ten recognized subspecies of eclectus parrot that likely all have slightly differing wild diets based on the geographical location they inhabit.[6] Eclectus have been noted to prefer fig type fruits in the wild, but seasonal variation of fruit availability plays a large role in what foods are preferred.[2]

When feeding eclectus in captivity we should pay attention to what they would likely be eating in the wild, but we do not have to fully mimic a bird's native diet in order to keep them healthy. The main staples of an eclectus parrot's diet in the wild can be interpreted to largely be green plant material, fruits, nuts and seeds. Wild eclectus require a dramatically higher number of calories a day than their captive counterparts. In captivity we can focus a large part of their diet on green plants, sprouted seeds, nutritious fruits and healthy nuts. Most veterinary professionals recommend that a formulated pellet diet makes up at least half of the captive eclectus diet, but a thoughtfully prepared fresh food diet can absolutely

Photo by Brandon Griggs

meet all of their nutritional requirements. There have not been any controlled studies looking at eclectus in particular and their dietary needs compared to other species of parrot. It has been suggested that eclectus parrots have a longer digestive tract than other parrots and require a less nutrient dense diet overall, but there have not to my knowledge been any published studies comparing the length of gastrointestinal tracts across all parrot species. Parrot species vary dramatically in habitat and native foods consumed, so there is a degree of guesswork when we call any diet complete for all parrots of a certain size or even geographic location.

Eclectus occasionally develop an unusual condition called "toe tapping and wing flapping" that causes them to uncontrollably tap their toes or flap their wings.[6] This condition is thought to be diet related, but there have been no specific studies that have been able to link this condition to a specific dietary imbalance. It has been hypothesized that eclectus do this in response to nutritionally inadequate diet – mainly low dietary calcium. However, there is an endless list of other potential culprits that have been suggested. There is absolutely no consensus among bird breeders, pet owners or even avian experts on what causes this, only a plethora of anecdotal reports. The most common suggestions for managing toe tapping and wing flapping are increasing calcium, removing processed foods from the diet and discontinuing using vitamin supplements.[6] Occasionally this condition is observed seasonally in some eclectus and thought to be a result of hormone changes.[6] It is likely that this condition has many causes that lead to one common presentation.

Generally what is agreed on is that eclectus thrive on a varied fresh food diet, supplemented with healthy dried and home-cooked foods, as well as an uncoloured high quality pellets (ideally cold pressed to preserve nutrients, rather than having vitamins added back in after heat processing). There should be a strong focus on providing a varied and rotating diet with an abundance of green vegetables, smaller amounts of fruits, sprouted seeds and healthy tree nuts. Make sure your bird is examined at least yearly by an avian veterinarian, if they have any symptoms of nutrient deficiencies at this time ask your veterinarian how best to treat your bird's condition. Weighing your bird weekly will help monitor how your bird is doing and help you notice any changes in their health before they become a severe issue.

Photo by Rigel

Works Cited:

[1] Brightsmith, Donald. "Cooperative Breeding in Parrots and Introduction to the Column Wild Science." *Bird Talk Magazine*, Oct. 1999.

[2] "Eclectus Parrot." *Parrots of the World*. Illustr. by William T. Cooper, by Joseph M. Forshaw, Doubleday, 1977, pp. 195–202.

[3] Heinsohn, Robert, et al. "Extreme Bias in Sex Allocation In Eclectus Parrots." Proceedings of the Royal Society of London. Series B: Biological Sciences, vol. 264, no. 1386, 1997, pp. 1325–1329., doi:10.1098/rspb.1997.0183.

[4] Heinsohn, Robert, and Sarah Legge. "Breeding Biology of the Reverse-Dichromatic, Co-Operative Parrot Eclectus Roratus." *Journal of Zoology*, vol. 259, no. 2, 28 Feb. 2006, pp. 197–208., doi:10.1017/s0952836902003138.

[5] Heinsohn, Robert, et al. "Genetic Evidence for Cooperative Polyandry in Reverse Dichromatic Eclectus Parrots." *Animal Behaviour*, vol. 74, no. 4, 2007, pp. 1047–1054., doi:10.1016/j.anbehav.2007.01.026.

[6] Marshall, Rob, and Ian Ward. *A Guide to Eclectus Parrots as Pet and Aviary Birds*. ABK Publications, 2004.

[7] Theuerkauf, Jörn, et al. "Cooperative Breeding, Mate Guarding, and Nest Sharing in Two Parrot Species of New Caledonia." *Journal of Ornithology*, vol. 150, no. 4, 2009, pp. 791–797., doi:10.1007/s10336-009-0400-8.

PROTEIN IN YOUR BIRD'S DIET

By Dr Stephanie Lamb, DVM

Proteins are macronutrients required by the body and are important for overall health. They are composed of individual units call amino acids which will combine together in different arrangements and lengths to make all the various protein macromolecules in living cells. There are 20 different amino acids, some of which are considered non-essential, meaning the body is able to make them on their own and they do not need to be provided in the diet. The remainder are essential, meaning they cannot be synthesized by the body and must be supplied in the diet. Birds, like many other animals, have 12 amino acids that are considered essential.

Once amino acids are combined together in larger protein units they are used by the body in various ways. They can be enzymes and transport molecules. They are involved in the immune system, control growth and cellular development, and are involved in transmitting nerve signals. They also provide structure and support to cells, tissues and organs. With the numerous important tasks proteins are required for, it is important they be supplied adequately in the diet for a bird to use.

Given this knowledge about proteins, the main question that bird owners may have is what amount should they provide in the diet for their bird? The answer to this is actually quiet variable. It depends on the species, age of the bird and reproductive status. Additionally, there are many species of birds

we don't know the specifics about, and further research is needed.

Generally, parrots are thought to need 10–24% of the diet as protein with the mean being 14–16%. Lorikeets, which are a nectivorous species, are unique among the parrots and require very low quantities of protein. They can do well on 3% protein if it is high quality.[1] Budgerigars require 10% protein in the diet.[2] Adult cockatiels on the other hand have been found to do well with protein as 11% of the diet.[1,3] Amazon parrots have been found to select diets that are 15.5% protein.[4] It is thought that larger parrots have a higher protein need than smaller species.[1]

When studies have looked at wild parrots the amount of protein they consume does vary slightly. Cockatiels will select food items that have a protein content that ranges from 8.8–14%. Little to none of this protein comes from animal matter.[3] Wild scarlet macaws will feed their young foods that have a protein content of 18–26%.[5]

The age of the bird does play a role in the amount of protein that they need. When birds are young they often require higher levels of protein in order to grow appropriately. If protein is restricted during this important time, growth will be slowed and their feathers will not develop as rapidly.[1] In cockatiels, diets that are 20% protein have been shown to be the most ideal for appropriate growth. Additionally, the specific amino acid lysine

Mealworms - animal-based protein

Quinoa - plant-based protein

needs to be 0.8–1.2% of the diet for optimal growth.[6]

Deficiencies in certain proteins can lead to weight loss, immunosuppression, loss of cell integrity and poor feather structure. When young cockatiels are growing, if they get only 5% protein in the diet they will be severely stunted. If they get protein levels at 10–15% of the diet, which are considered appropriate for an adult, their growth will be slightly stunted and slower than normal.[6] For adult birds, if the amino acid methionine is deficient in the diet it can result in changes like fatty liver syndrome, stress bars in feathers, and a lack of the normal blue or green colour to feathers.[7]

Excessive protein in the diet can be a problem as well. Lesions have been identified in the liver of birds consuming too high a level of protein. Inflammatory cells with fatty deposits have been found in adult cockatiels getting 20, 35 and 70% protein in the diet with severity of the lesions increasing as the protein level increased.[3] In growing cockatiels a slight increase in protein to 25%, which is just above the ideal level, results in refusal of feed and aggression. Higher levels at 35% will result in slower growth rate and increased aggression.[6] There has been suspicion that high protein in the diet could cause kidney disease or gout. However, research shows that when cockatiels are given diets with protein up to 70%, this does not occur. Kidney values on blood work may increase but it is not

Photo by Renan Brun

necessarily correlated with kidney disease.[3]

One important point to make about protein for pet parrots is that this nutrient should be from plant sources. In the wild, parrots do not eat much in the way of animal-based food items. They may occasionally eat an insect, and if they do it is typically around breeding season. Therefore, in captivity, we should focus on getting parrots their protein from plant-based sources.

So, what foods are good for supplying protein to pet parrots? If you are feeding a lot of fresh items, it is important to know which items are good sources of protein. Certain foods are known to have higher levels of protein than others. Cooked or sprouted beans, legumes, grains, nuts and seeds fall into this category.

One grain that is a great source of protein is quinoa. This grain is 16% protein and is considered complete, meaning it has all the essential amino acids. Many pet birds readily eat this grain, even those small picky eaters, since it is small and the size of a millet seed. Lentils are another great protein source and have 36% protein. These are often best accepted when they are cooked.

Although various beans, seeds and nuts supply ample sources of protein, one thing to keep in mind is that many are not complete protein sources. This means that they will not supply adequate amounts of all the different amino acids by themselves. However, different foods will have different amino acid contents; therefore, it is important that there are a variety of protein rich foods offered so there is a greater likelihood of attaining a balance of the individual amino acids. People have already created great combinations of foods that do this. For example, many cooked or sprouted beans and grains are often combined to make delicious meals but also provide a protein balanced diet.

For example, mung beans supply a good amount of protein; however, they are lower in the amino acids methionine and cysteine.[8] In order to get these amino acids to make a complete and balanced meal, another protein source that is high in methionine and cysteine may be given. Examples of foods containing these amino acids in greater amounts include Brazil nuts, cooked black beans, squash seeds or edamame.[9] A combination of these foods for a pet bird can provide a tasty and protein balanced meal.

In conclusion, proteins play an important role in a bird's nutrition and health. Owners need to not only provide appropriate amounts of protein in the diet based on their individual bird's needs but they also need to provide the appropriate balance of individual amino acids.

Works Cited:

1. Koutsos, E., Gelis, S., and Echols, M.S. (2016). "Advancements in nutrition and nutritional therapy." In B.L. Speer (ed.), *Current Therapy in Avian Medicine and Surgery* (pp.142–176). Elsevier.

2. Harper, J., and Skinner, N.D. (1998). "Clinical nutrition of small psittacines and passerines." *Semi Exot Pet Med* 7: 116–127.

3. Koutsos, E.A., Smith, J., Woods, L.W., and Klasing, K.C. (2001). "Adult cockatiels metabolically adapt to high protein diets." *J Nutr*, 131(7), 2014–2020.

4. Brightsmith, D.J. (2012). "Nutritional levels of diets fed to captive Amazon parrots: Does mixing seed, produce and pellets provide a healthy diet?" *J Avian Med Surg*, 26(3), 149–160.

5. Brightsmith, D., McDonald, D., Matsafuji, D., and Bailey, C.A. (2010). "Nutritional content of the diets of free-living scarlet macaw chicks in southeastern Peru." *J Avian Med Surg*, 24(1), 9–23.

6. Brue, R.N. (1994). "Nutrition." In Ritchie, Harrison, Harrison (eds), *Avian Medicine: Principles and Applications* (pp.63–95). Wingers Publishing Inc.

7. Macwhirter, P. (1994). "Malnutrition." In Ritchie, Harrison, Harrison (eds), *Avian Medicine: Principles and Applications* (pp.842–861). Wingers Publishing Inc.

8. Yi-Shen, Z., Shuai, S., and FitzGerald, R. (2018). "Mung bean proteins and peptides: nutritional, functional, and bioactive properties." *Food Nutr Res*, 62. 10.29219/fnr.v62.1290.

9. (2018). *Self Nutrition* Data. https://nutritiondata.self.com/

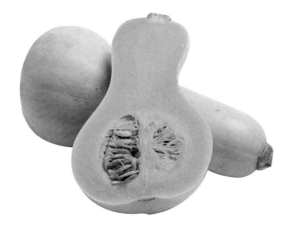

FEATHER DISORDERS AND DIETARY LINKS

By Dr Stephanie Lamb, DVM

Abnormal feathers are a concern for many companion bird owners because alterations in the feathers' appearance can be linked to internal problems at times. Dull, discoloured, broken or tattered feathers and abnormal molting cycles are all issues that can be seen. One common feather problem that plagues the pet bird population though is feather destructive behaviours, also known as feather picking or plucking. This is a frustrating and multifactorial disorder that can be caused by so many different underlying problems it is impossible to pinpoint just one cause to its development. One way to look at feather picking causes is that they can fall into one of two broad categories – pathologic or behavioural.

Pathologic causes are going to be various diseases or disorders. The following is a list of the various problems that fall into the pathologic category and have been seen associated with feather picking.

Infectious disease

> **Bacterial infections:** On the skin, in the gastrointestinal tract, in the respiratory system, or systemically

> **Fungal infections:** On the skin (*Candida* sp., *Malasezia* sp.), in the gastrointestinal tract (*Candida* sp., *Macrorhabdus ornithogaster*) or respiratory system (*Aspergillus* sp.)

> **Parasitic infections:** On the skin (Knemidokoptes, red mites) or in the gastrointestinal tract (*Spironucleus meleagridis*)

> **Viral infections:** Avian bornavirus (The viruses polyoma and psittacine beak and feather disease tend to cause feather changes but not necessarily self-induced picking)

Metabolic disorders

> Liver disease and kidney disease

Musculoskeletal pain

> Trauma, fractures, dislocations, muscle sprain or strains

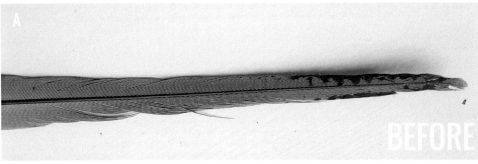

A - combination of seed-based, processed and other species inappropriate diet

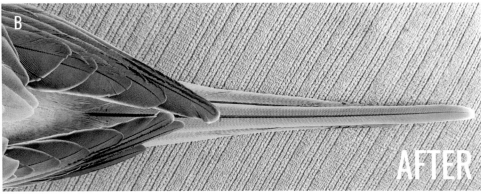

B - raw whole food diet

Nutritional

> Deficiencies: Vitamin A deficiency, lack of certain proteins or B vitamins

> Excesses: High fat and calories could lead to other problems

Neoplastic

> Xanthomas can be itchy

> Various cancers that could cause pain or discomfort could induce picking

Toxins

> Lead, zinc, copper, airway irritants

> Foreign object ingestion

> Hormonal disorders

Allergy

> This is a very controversial idea in birds but something to mention as it may occasionally be a factor

Behavioural causes are very common as well, and with these issues there is some sort of stress that is causing them to direct their attention to pick at their own feathers.
The following is a list of common behavioural causes for picking that are seen.

Reproductive/Hormonal stress

> Small amounts of picking to create a "brood patch" could be considered normal but it can go on to excess and result in unnatural amounts of feather loss.

Boredom

> A lack of mental stimulation with toys or foraging activities could cause a bird to focus its behaviours on grooming and start to do it to excess.

> A monotonous environment that never changes could lead to picking.

General anxiety

> Barking dogs, prowling cats, or humans who don't understand how to read bird body language and overstep a bird's comfort level could all induce feather picking behaviours.

> Sometimes the smallest change in the environment could be stressful to a bird and result in feather picking.

Reinforcement of picking by human companions

> Sometimes people can inadvertently reinforce their bird to pick by paying extra attention to their bird when they pick, thus encouraging picking because the bird gets attention when picking.

When a bird starts to feather pick itself, all the above causes need to be considered and owners need to ask themselves lots of questions to find out what could be the cause for their individual pet. A visit with a veterinarian who is competent in avian behaviour is often recommended to help counsel an owner on what might need to be done for the bird. An examination and in-depth questioning would be part of the evaluation but other things like

diagnostic tests may or may not be necessary for the individual bird. Blood work, skin cytologies, radiographs, toxin or specific infectious disease testing may be needed.

If there is a pathologic cause for the feather picking then treatment focused on fixing that is needed. If on the other hand, a behavioural cause is more likely, then work on modifying the behaviour is needed. If there is some generalized anxiety, and a specific stressor can be pinpointed, it needs to be addressed and altered. Additionally, making sure the bird has some way to redirect its attention to more appropriate behaviours has been found to be helpful for many causes of feather picking.

Good ways to do this are through having access to toys that the bird actually enjoys and interacts with, trick training and foraging.

Although direct links may not be readily apparent, nutrition can play a role in feather picking in some cases and therefore, this is something that owners can work on at home to avoid problems in their pet parrots. As mentioned above, nutritional deficiencies or excesses can occur that lead to feather problems.

For starters, vitamin A deficiencies are commonly seen in birds, and the classic diet that results in this disorder is the all-seed diet. Seeds naturally lack this nutrient and with time, vitamin A deficiencies will cause changes to the cells that line the skin, along with cells that line other parts of the body. This could potentially result in dry skin and poor feather development, both of which may stimulate a bird to pick. Providing foods that are high in vitamin A, or their precursors, several times a week can help reduce this possible problem.

Additionally, there have been various B vitamin deficiencies linked to the development of abnormal feathers. In cockatiels, deficiencies in riboflavin (vitamin B2) and choline have been seen with a condition known as achromatosis. This is where there is a failure of the body to lay down normal feather pigment in the developing feather. Additionally, the various other B vitamins play many roles in the body's normal metabolic pathways and if they are lacking, various disorders could occur. These may lead to secondary skin or feather changes that may result in a bird having poor feathering and possibly picking at them.

Next, protein deficiencies have the potential to lead to disorders that could stimulate feather picking. Seed-based diets are often lacking in methionine and lysine, both proteins that when low, could lead to the development of liver problems, particularly fatty liver syndrome. A malfunctioning liver can cause numerous other disorders which may secondarily lead to a bird feather picking.

On the other hand, nutritional excesses could lead to problems that result in a bird feather picking. Excess amounts of fat in the diet lead to an abundance of calories and if a bird doesn't need the extra calories it is something that could stimulate the bird's hormonal drive. Combined with other stimuli, reproductive drive could occur excessively and feather picking disorders have certainly been associated with this problem before. Additionally, for some species high moisture foods may stimulate hormonal drive and thus food presented in this manner may need to be avoided to avoid hormonal issues from occurring.

There is not a straightforward answer for feather picking. There are so many variables that could be present, so each bird really needs to be treated as an individual for why it is picking. Of course, a balanced diet is always recommended to help keep a bird healthy and even treat certain problems. However, with feather picking, evaluation by a veterinarian, providing low stress, and incorporating activities that redirect a bird's attention to more appropriate behaviours is often a part of dealing with the complex problem of feather picking.

FEEDING FRUITS TO YOUR PARROT

Fruits provide vital nutrients for your bird and should be part of their daily diverse diet. They are rich in antioxidants, vitamins and minerals and offer a great source of important nutrients such as vitamin C which helps to boost their immune system, a dietary fibre that helps your bird's digestive system functioning properly and folic acid that helps the body make healthy red blood cells. Fruits are also water-rich foods that will help your bird stay hydrated and are refreshing during hot summer days.

When it comes to offering fruits to your bird, ideally they should not form more than 10% of their diet as some can be high in natural sugars, with the exception of some specific species where fruits form the main part of the bird's diet. Birds do enjoy eating fruits and that is probably one thing we can say they are not fussy about as it is a highly palatable food for them. You may see them picking the dried fruit out of the seed mixes first as opposed to the seeds. The downside is that birds are often fed more fruits than they should be, which in the long term may contribute to some health problems if the diet lacks in other nutrients.

Fruits contain natural sugars that may give your bird an energy boost. At some point the body converts the sugars into fat and this get stored in the liver. If the bird has no or limited exercise to work it off, this can build up over time causing fatty liver disease. No matter what type of food they eat, their body still needs to move in order to be healthy.

Some parrot owners tend to feed only fruits for breakfast. This is not the best approach as the focus should be on offering more nutritional breakfast that consists of a variety of fresh vegetables, herbs, sprouts, soaked seeds and nuts rather than just fruits. Fruits shouldn't be the predominant part of the bird's diet but are absolutely essential and needed as part of their diverse daily diet.

Seeds in fruits

Some fruits' seeds are very healthy and beneficial for your parrot and can be a great foraging opportunity.

Safe fruit seeds you can offer to your parrot are: papaya seeds, seeds from melons, such as cantaloupe, casaba, canary, crenshaw, honeydrew, pepino and watermelon. These can be offered to forage on directly from the fruit or you can scoop the flesh out and put it into their bowls.

Fruit smoothies and juices

Be careful about offering fruit smoothies or freshly squeezed juices as they are little sugar bombs.

Photo by David Clode

Below are some of the fruits we usually offer ranked highest to lowest in overall sugar content.

Fruits highest in sugars	Sugar per 100g
Jackfruit	31g (7.8 tsp)
Persimmon	21g (5.3 tsp)
Grapes	16g (4.1 tsp)
Litchis (Lychees)	15g (3.8 tsp)
Pomegranate	14g (3.4 tsp)
Mangos	14g (3.4 tsp)
Cherries	13g (3.2 tsp)
Bananas	12g (3.1 tsp)
Passion Fruit	11g (2.8 tsp)
Pears	10g (2.4 tsp)
Apples	10g (2.6 tsp)
Oranges	9g (2.3 tsp)
Kiwi	9g (2.2 tsp)
Guavas	9g (2.2 tsp)
Peaches	8g (2.1 tsp)
Papaya	8g (2 tsp)
Nectarines	8g (2 tsp)

However, this doesn't mean you should now completely stop feeding these types of fruits to your birds, absolutely not, but just keep in mind that they should be offered in moderation.

Fruits high in water

> Watermelon – 92% water content

> Strawberries – 91% water content

> Cantaloupe – 90% water content

> Peaches – 89% water content

> Oranges – 88% water content

> Grapefruit – 88% water content (offer in moderation)

Tips when feeding fruits:

> Avoid canned fruits as these can be high in artificial sugar and may contain some preservatives. Vitamin C is heat sensitive and can be destroyed in the canning process. Nothing beats fresh fruit.

> Avoid commercially produced fruit smoothies as they are high in sugars and may contain preservatives. Some juices are not 100% freshly squeezed and are made from a concentrate so it's likely they'll contain preservatives, other high-calorie additives or added sugars that your bird doesn't need.

› Frozen fruit is fine.

› When offering fresh fruits, make sure they are ripe.

› Same piece of fruit daily will not provide the nutrients your bird needs so offer different varieties.

› Always wash the fruit thoughtfully as some are part of the "Dirty Dozen" group – such as strawberries, pears, grapes, cherries, nectarines, peaches and apples. It's not necessary to take the skin off some fruits such as apples or pears if properly washed as the peel contains some nutrients too.

› Be careful with fruits that have pits/seeds as the majority are not safe for parrots and need to be removed, e.g. seeds from apples, pears, cherries or pits from nectarines and peaches.

› Never offer any food that was once dropped at the bottom of the cage as it may have been contaminated with faeces and other bacteria.

› Fruits such as grapes are a great treat as part of training.

› Careful when offering any dried fruits as those are little sugar bombs.

› Never leave any fruit in your bird's bowl overnight as it will spoil, especially during the summer.

Good to know

Feeding processed food that is high in refined sugar (usually labelled as sucrose, corn sugar or corn syrup) may promote various infections, such as Candida albicans or may result in the hyperactivity, promote feather picking, cancer, obesity, some mineral imbalance, high cholesterol levels, irritability, anxiety, manifestation of diabetes.

UNDERSTANDING PLANT OILS IN YOUR BIRD'S DIET

By Dr Stephanie Lamb, DVM

When people discuss nutrition, oils often get a bad rap. However, they are a macronutrient just like proteins and carbohydrates, and are just as essential. Also known as fats, they have various functions including acting as an energy source, insulating cells and tissues, acting as hormones, aiding in the absorption of vitamins, and acting in cellular signalling pathways. Without them, the body would cease to function appropriately. On the other hand, too many fats can be problematic. Therefore, like all other nutrients, getting the right balance of fats in the diet is necessary for appropriate health.

There are many different forms fats and oils can come as, including free fatty acids, triglycerides and cholesterol to name a few. Fatty acids are chains that are composed of links of carbon molecules strung together with hydrogen atoms branching off them. Three fatty acid chains will bind to a molecule called glycerol to form a triglyceride. The fatty acid chains vary in how they are named and it is dependent upon their length and how the carbon atoms are bound together. When considering their length, they are categorized as short chain, medium chain or long chain. The way the carbon atoms bind together will further classify them as saturated or unsaturated. Unsaturated fatty acids mean there are double bonds between carbon atoms, while saturated fatty acids have no double bonds between their carbon atoms. Unsaturated fatty acids can further be classified as monounsaturated, meaning there is only one double bond between carbon atoms in the fatty acid chain, or polyunsaturated, meaning there are multiple double bonds along the fatty acid chain. Omega-3 and omega-6 fatty acids are examples of unsaturated fatty acids. This variation of fats contributes to how the fats function in the body and what their health benefits can be.

Fats can come from plant and animal sources. They can be provided in the diet through whole food items or they can be supplemented as liquid oils. Pet psittacine birds should be having the majority of their fats and oils supplied to them from a plant source. Occasionally, animal-based oils will be beneficial for certain medical disorders, but this is something that should be discussed with an animal health care professional. Therefore, for most pet bird owners at home, they should stick with using a plant-based source of oil for their birds.

Plant oils that are commonly available include flax oil, coconut oil, chia oil, and red palm oil. They are all a little different in the type of fat that they provide and how they may be beneficial to the body.

Photo by Roberto Nickson

Flax oil

Flax oil comes from the flaxseed. It is a polyunsaturated fatty acid and is high in the omega-3 fatty acid alpha-linolenic acid. Omega-3 fatty acids are touted to have various health benefits including anti-inflammatory effects, anti-thrombotic (blood clotting) properties, and may be helpful in preventing cardiovascular disease. They reduce the concentration of several molecules involved in cell signalling pathways that lead to the development the devastating heart disease atherosclerosis.[1] One study found that parrots that lacked atherosclerotic lesions in their cardiovascular system had higher levels of alpha-linolenic acid in their breast muscle and fat tissues. The researchers of this paper suggested that high dietary intake of alpha-linolenic acid may protect against the development of atherosclerosis in parrots.[2]

Coconut oil

Coconut oil

Coconut oil comes from coconuts and is higher in saturated fats than the other oils mentioned. This is what allows for it to be a solid when it is cool. Saturated fats can stick together tighter and form solid structures while unsaturated fats have lots of bends in the links of carbon atoms that compose them and therefore cannot pack together as tightly. This makes it so unsaturated fatty acids cannot form a solid structure and instead stay as a liquid. Generally, saturated fats are less desirable in the diet because they are more calorically dense. However, some saturated fats are acceptable.

Coconut oil is often considered to be desirable as a fat because it is composed of various compounds including medium chain triglycerides (or fatty acid chains). These are absorbed and metabolized through a different route than other fats which can be beneficial for certain disorders. Additionally, there is some data to support the suggestion

Flaxseeds

that the other fat compounds in the oil have antioxidant properties and may reduce certain types of cholesterol in the blood.[3] Studies have not been carried out on birds to support these attributes but may be true for them as they are in mammals.

Chia oil

Chia oil comes from the chia seed. This oil is also high in omega-3 fatty acids with a ratio of 3:1 for omega-3 to omega-6. Therefore, it may have some similar health benefits to flaxseed oil when given to birds. Studies have been carried out on chickens that show when they get this in their diet, alpha-linolenic acid levels are significantly higher in their breast muscles. It also lowered the amount of saturated fatty acid in the muscle and omega-6:omega-3 ratio.[4] All these changes could be beneficial for reducing the cardiovascular disease, atherosclerosis.

Red palm oil

Palm oil comes from the fruit of the African oil palm tree. The main form that has health benefits is red palm oil. This form of palm oil incorporates a water-soluble component that would normally be wasted in the milling process. There are several carotene compounds present in this that act as antioxidants and as precursors to vitamin A, both of which could be beneficial in various ailments. However, palm oil is high in omega-6 fatty acids which are pro-inflammatory.[5] Studies in chickens show it will improve consumption of food and weight gain.[6] Therefore, use of this type of oil may be considered more sparingly and only for specific needs.

Conclusion

Oils are not only essential nutrients, but they can also be used to promote health and possibly even prevent and treat certain disorders. Understanding the different types of oils that are available and what nutrients they provide can help a pet bird owner in selecting the right one for their bird. Every bird is an individual and providing them with the right nutrition for their needs is essential for health and happiness.

Works Cited:
1. Petzinger, C., Heatley, J.J., Cornejo, J., Brightsmith, D.J., and Bauer, J.E. (2010). "Dietary modification of omega-3 fatty acids for birds with atherosclerosis." *J Am Vet Med Asso*, 236(5), 523–528.
2. Bavelaar, F.J., and Beynen, A.C. (2003). "Severity of atherosclerosis in parrots in relation to the intake of alpha-linolenic acid." *Avian Dis*, 47(3), 566–577.
3. Carandang, E.V. (2008). "Health benefits of virgin coconut oil." *Indian Coconut Journal*, 8–12.
4. Ayerza, R., Coates, W., and Lauria, M. (2002). "Chia seed (*Salvia hispanica L.*) as an omega-3 fatty acid source for broilers: influence on fatty acid composition, cholesterol and fat content of white and dark meats, growth performance, and sensory characteristics." *Poult Sci*, 81(6), 826–837.
5. Moran, L. (2017, April). "The Holistic Parrot: Red Palm Oil." Parrots Magazine, 232, 12–15.
6. Rahman, M., Akbar, M., Islam, K., Iqbal, A., and Assaduzzaman, M. (2010). "Effect of dietary inclusion of palm oil on feed consumption, growth performance and profitability of broiler." *Bangladesh Journal Animal Science*, 39(1–2), 176–182.

ESSENTIAL VITAMINS AND MINERALS IN PARROTS

By Dr Stephanie Lamb, DVM and Karmen Budai

Different vitamins and minerals are required in a bird's diet to ensure adequate health and longevity. Below is a list of essential vitamins and minerals and a description of their function within the body. Sources of these nutrients are also listed so owners can ensure they are providing appropriate levels for their birds.

VITAMINS

Vitamin A

Importance: Needed by cells that line the skin, mucous membranes, glandular tissue and organs such as the kidneys and reproductive tract.

Deficiency: Can lead to respiratory tract, kidney and reproductive tract disorders. It can also lead to reduced immunity and a reduced ability to prevent colonization by pathogens. Drowsiness, incoordination, impaired vision and emaciation can occur as well.

Excess: Can cause hyperexcitability, increased vocalizations, pancreatitis and an impaired antibody response.

Suggested sources:

Vegetables: Bok choy (pak choi), broccoli, Brussels sprouts, butternut squash, carrot, chilli pepper, collard greens, dandelion leaves, green beans, green peas, kale, pumpkin, red pepper, rocket (arugula), romaine lettuce, spinach, sweet potato, Swiss chard, turnip greens, watercress.

Fruits: Apricot, canary melon, cantaloupe melon, gooseberries, grapefruit, mango, nectarine, palm fruit (nuts), papaya, passion fruit, peach, persimmon (kaki), plantains (yellow and green), plum, tamarillo, watermelon.

Fresh Herbs: Basil, coriander (cilantro), dill, mint, oregano, parsley, rosemary, sage, thyme.
Other: Sprouted legumes and grains.

Vitamin C

Importance: Needed for the immune system, cardiovascular system and helps for growth and repairing tissues.
Deficiency: Most birds can make this on their own so deficiencies are unlikely, but for those species that do require it in the diet you can see scurvy (haemorrhages) if they don't have it.
Excess: As a water-soluble vitamin, excessive amounts are excreted so toxicities do not occur.

Suggested sources:
Vegetables: Bok choy (pak choi), broccoli, Brussels sprouts, butternut squash, cauliflower, chilli pepper, collard greens, corn (raw), courgette (zucchini), dandelion leaves, fennel, green beans, green peas, kale, okra, pumpkin, radish, red pepper, rocket (arugula), romaine lettuce, spinach, sweet potato, Swiss chard, turnip greens, watercress, yams.
Fruits: Apple, apricot, banana, blackberry, blackcurrant, blueberry, boysenberry, canary melon, cantaloupe melon, carambola (star fruit), casaba melon, cranberry, crenshaw melon, cherry, dragon fruit (pitaya), gooseberries, grapefruit, guava, honeydew melon, kiwi, lychees (litchis), mango, mangosteen, nectarine, orange, palm fruit (nuts), papaya, passion fruit, peach, pear, persimmon (kaki), pineapple, plantains (yellow and green), plum, pomegranate, raspberry, red currants, strawberry, tamarillo, tangerines (mandarin), watermelon.

Herbs: Basil, coriander (cilantro), dill, mint, parsley, red clover, rosemary, sage, star anise, thyme.

Vitamin D

Importance: Required for normal calcium metabolism which is important for growth, reproduction, bone health, muscle health and nervous system health.
Deficiency: Can lead to rickets or osteomalacia which is a softening of the bones that can lead to abnormal bends and malformation of the bones along with fractures. It can also lead to impaired egg laying, thin shelled eggs, and signs associated with low calcium such as muscle weakness and nervous system deficits.
Excess: Can lead to mineralization of soft tissues, particularly the kidneys.

Note: The best way for a bird to get vitamin D is NOT through dietary sources but by allowing the bird to make it on its own by being out in the sun or exposed to a UVB light. Allow your bird to access natural sunlight for at least 15 minutes a day in order to get vitamin D produced via absorption of sunlight.

Vitamin E

Importance: Functions as an antioxidant and also is important for normal nervous system and muscle health.
Deficiency: Can lead to neurologic problems, muscle disorders, poor reproduction and skin problems.
Excess: Can result in anaemia (low red blood cells), poor growth, and impair the liver's ability to store vitamin A. The bones can be poorly mineralized as well.

Suggested sources:
Vegetables: Butternut squash, red pepper, Swiss chard, turnip greens.
Fruit: Apricots, cranberry, kiwi, mango, palm fruit (nuts), raspberry.
Other: Almonds, Brazil nuts, hazelnuts, pecans, pine nuts, pumpkin seeds, sunflower seeds.

Vitamin K

Importance: Needed for clotting blood appropriately.
Deficiency: Can result in blood clotting disorders.

Excess: Can result in anaemia (low red blood cells) and can interfere with the functioning of other vitamins.

Suggested sources:
Vegetables: Artichoke, bok choy (pak choi), Brussels sprouts, carrot, cauliflower, collard greens, cucumber, dandelion leaves, green beans, green peas, kale, rocket (arugula), romaine lettuce, spinach, Swiss chard, turnip greens, watercress.
Fruits: Blackberry, blueberry, cherry, fig (raw), grape, kiwi, pear, plum, pomegranate, raspberry.
Herbs: Basil, coriander (cilantro), oregano, parsley, sage.
Other: Cashews, pine nuts.

Vitamin B1 (Thiamine)

Importance: Needed for normal nervous system functioning and cardiovascular health. It helps in the metabolism of carbohydrates.
Deficiency: Can result in neurologic disorders like weakness, paresis, paralysis and convulsions.
Excess: As a water-soluble vitamin, excessive amounts are excreted so toxicities do not occur.

Suggested sources:
Vegetables and Fruits: Acai berry, acorn squash, Brussels sprouts, corn (raw), green peas, sweet potato, watermelon, yams.
Other: Barley (soaked or sprouted), Brazil nuts, brown rice (cooked), flaxseeds (linseeds), lentils (soaked or sprouted), pecans, pine nuts, sunflower seeds.

Vitamin B2 (Riboflavin)

Importance: Needed for carbohydrate metabolism.
Deficiency: Can cause achromatosis in cockatiels. This is a loss of normal pigmentation to the feathers. It can also cause a reduction of eggs in a clutch and reduced hatching of eggs. In some species of birds, like chickens, it can cause a condition known as curled toe paralysis, impaired growth, paralysis and diarrhoea.
Excess: As a water-soluble vitamin, excessive amounts are excreted so toxicities do not occur.

Suggested sources:
Acai berry, almonds, apple, courgette (zucchini), dill, dragon fruit (pitaya), dried date, eggs, spinach, sweet potato, Swiss chard.

Vitamin B3 (Niacin)

Importance: Needed as a cofactor for enzymes involved in carbohydrate, fat and protein metabolism. The enzymes it contributes to also helps with cell signalling and DNA repair.
Deficiency: Can cause scaly dermatitis and disorders of the hock joint in chickens. In other animals it can cause pellagra which results in diarrhoea, inflamed skin and discolouration to the tongue.
Excess: As a water-soluble vitamin, excessive amounts are excreted so toxicities do not occur, however, in other animals you can see diarrhoea, itching and flushing of the skin.
Suggested sources: Almonds, barley grain (soaked or sprouted), brown rice (cooked), dill, green peas, pine nuts, sunflower seeds, sweet potato, wheat grain (soaked or sprouted).

Vitamin B4 (Choline)

Some refer to choline as vitamin B4 while others do not. It has been decided to include it here, however.

Importance: Acts as a precursor to neurotransmitters that are needed for normal nervous system signalling. It also plays a role in cell membrane signalling and transport of fats.

Deficiency: Has been implicated in perosis (slipped tendon) in chickens. Deficiency may also result in liver disease, a cardiovascular disorder known as atherosclerosis and neurologic disease.

Excess: As a water-soluble vitamin, excessive amounts are excreted so toxicities do not occur.

Photo by Francesco Califano

Suggested sources:
Apple, broccoli, brown rice (cooked), caraway seeds, eggs, ginger, oats, strawberries.

Vitamin B5 (Pantothenic Acid)

Importance: Functions as a component of coenzyme A which is needed for carbohydrate, fat and protein metabolism.

Deficiency: Impairs growth, results in abnormal feather development, and can lead to dermatitis and death.

Excess: As a water-soluble vitamin, excessive amounts are excreted so toxicities do not occur.

Suggested sources:
Broccoli, dill, egg yolk, grapefruit, lentils (soaked or sprouted), pineapple, sunflower seeds, sweet potatoes.

Vitamin B6 (Pyridoxine)

Importance: Important in carbohydrate, protein and fat metabolism. It also is involved in the production of neurotransmitters (signals between nerves) and immune function.

Deficiency: These are unlikely but can lead to reduced appetite, neurologic signs, anaemia (low red blood cells), slow growth and dermatitis.

Excess: As a water-soluble vitamin, excessive amounts are excreted so toxicities do not occur.

Suggested sources:
Vegetables: Corn (raw), courgette (zucchini), red pepper, sweet potato, yams.

Fruits: Banana, cherry, honeydew melon, mango, pineapple, plantains (yellow and green), tangerines, watermelon.
Herbs: Dill, rosemary.
Other: Flaxseeds (linseeds), hazelnuts, lentils (soaked or sprouted), pistachios (unsalted), sesame seeds, sunflower seeds.

Vitamin B7 (Biotin)

Importance: Works as a coenzyme for carbohydrate, fat and protein metabolism.
Deficiency: Can lead to dermatitis, toe necrosis, swollen eyelids, perosis (slipped hock) and has also been implicated in fatty liver and kidney syndrome.
Excess: As a water-soluble vitamin, excessive amounts are excreted so toxicities do not occur.

Suggested sources:
Almonds, bananas, cauliflower, egg yolks, raspberry, walnuts, whole grains.

Vitamin B9 (Folic Acid)

Importance: Works as a cofactor in the synthesis of purines (a component of DNA).
Deficiency: Results in slow growth, poor feathering, anaemia (low red blood cells), reduced egg production and hatchability, and bone abnormalities in embryos and growing birds.
Excess: As a water-soluble vitamin, excessive amounts are excreted so toxicities do not occur.

Suggested sources:
Vegetables: Artichoke, beetroot, broccoli, Brussels sprouts, cauliflower, corn (raw), kale, okra, spinach, watercress.
Fruits: Banana, guava, orange, pear, pineapple, strawberry, raw coconut (flesh and water).
Herbs: Sage.
Other: Legumes, nuts, quinoa, seeds.

Vitamin B12 (Cobalamin)

Importance: Functions as a coenzyme and is involved in fat and protein metabolism and the synthesis of DNA.
Deficiency: Anaemia (low red blood cells) has been reported in parrots. Perosis (slipped tendon), gizzard erosions and fatty liver, heart and kidneys have been seen in chickens.
Excess: As a water-soluble vitamin, excessive amounts are excreted so toxicities do not occur.

Suggested sources:
Eggs.*

Note
The main source is probably more dependent upon the intrinsic abilities of the bird to make this nutrient, or rather, the bird's appropriate healthy gut microbiome. In other species we know that having bacterial flora in the gut that are healthy will result in the production of appropriate vitamin B12. This is likely to be the case for birds as well.

Eggs should only be fed sparingly and must always be cooked.

MINERALS

Calcium

Suggested sources:
Vegetables: Beetroot, bok choy (pak choi), broccoli, butternut squash, cauliflower, collard greens, cucumber, dandelion leaves, dill, fennel, kale, okra, rocket (arugula), turnip greens, watercress.
Fruits: Acai berry, apple, banana, blackcurrant, date, fig (raw), mangosteen, mulberry, orange, pear, pineapple, red currants, tangerine.
Herbs: Basil, Ceylon cinnamon bark, chamomile, cloves, coriander (cilantro), mint, oregano, parsley, red clover, rosemary, sage, star anise, thyme.
Other: Almonds, chia seeds, coconut water (fresh), wheat grain (soaked or sprouted).

Copper

Suggested sources:
Vegetables: Beetroot, dandelion leaves, fennel, Swiss chard, turnip greens, yams.

Fruits: Acai berry, apricot, blackberry, blueberry, butternut squash, cherry, coconut (flesh), cranberry, gooseberries, grape, guava, kiwi, lychees (litchis), mango, nectarine, pear, persimmon (kaki), plum, raspberry, red currants, tangerines (mandarin), watermelon.
Herbs : Thyme.
Other: Almonds, Brazil nuts, cashews, chia seeds, chickpeas, hazelnuts, lentils (soaked or sprouted), pecans, pine nuts, pumpkin seeds, quinoa, sesame seed, sunflower seeds.

Iodine

Suggested sources:
Vegetables: Watercress.
Other : Eggs, whole grains.

Iron

Suggested sources:
Vegetables: Artichoke, beetroot, bok choy (pak choi), Brussels sprouts, corn, dandelion leaves, fennel, green peas, okra, pumpkin, spinach, sweet potato, Swiss chard, watercress.

Fruits: Acai berry, apple, banana, blackcurrant, boysenberry, carambola (star fruit), date, dragon fruit (pitaya), mangosteen, mulberry, passion fruit, peach, persimmon (kaki), plantains (yellow and green), raspberry, red currants, tamarillo.
Herbs: Ceylon cinnamon bark, cloves, coriander (cilantro), dill, mint, oregano, parsley, rosemary, sage, star anise, thyme.
Other: Brazil nuts, cashews, coconut water (from raw coconut), pine nuts, pumpkin seeds.

Magnesium

Suggested sources:
Vegetables: Artichoke, beetroot, bok choy (pak choi), broccoli, corn (raw), butternut squash, cauliflower, cucumber, dandelion leaves, fennel, kale, okra, rocket (arugula), spinach, Swiss chard, watercress.
Fruits: Acai berry, apple, banana, blackberry, blackcurrant, boysenberry, carambola (star fruit), cantaloupe melon, cherry, dragon fruit (pitaya), fig (raw), grapefruit, guava, lychees (litchis), mulberry, orange, papaya, peach, pear, pineapple, plantains (yellow and green),

plum, raspberry, strawberry, tangerine, watermelon.
Herbs: Basil, chamomile, cloves, coriander (cilantro), mint, parsley, red clover, rosemary, sage, star anise, thyme.
Other: Almonds, barley, Brazil nuts, brown rice (cooked), cashews, coconut (water and flesh), flaxseeds (linseeds), hazelnuts, lentils (soaked or sprouted), oats, pine nuts, pumpkin seeds, quinoa, sunflower seeds, wheat grain (soaked or sprouted).

Phosphorus

Suggested sources:
Vegetables: Artichoke, bok choy (pak choi), broccoli, Brussels sprouts, corn (raw), cucumber, kale, radish, rocket (arugula), watercress.
Fruits: Apple, blackcurrant, carambola (star fruit), fig (raw), guava, lychees (litchis), mulberry, plum, pomegranate, tamarillo.
Herbs: Red clover, star anise.
Other: Almonds, Brazil nuts, brown rice (cooked), cashews, chia seeds, flaxseeds (linseeds), oats, pine nuts, pumpkin seeds, quinoa, wheat grain (soaked or sprouted).

Potassium

Suggested sources:
Vegetables: Acorn squash, artichoke, beetroot, bell pepper, broccoli, Brussels sprouts, carrot, cauliflower, corn (raw), courgette (zucchini), cucumber, dandelion leaves, fennel, green peas, kale, okra, pumpkin, radish, spinach, sweet potato, Swiss chard, winter squash, yams.
Fruits: Apple, apricot, banana, blackberry, blackcurrant, blueberry, boysenberry, cantaloupe melon, carambola (star fruit), casaba melon, cherry, coconut flesh, cranberry, date, fig (raw), gooseberries, grapefruit, grapes, guava, honeydew melon, kiwi, lychees (litchis), mango, mulberry, nectarine, orange, papaya, passion fruit, peach, pear, persimmon (kaki), pineapple, plantains (yellow and green), plum, pomegranate, strawberry, tamarillo, tangerine (mandarin), watermelon.
Herbs: Ceylon cinnamon bark, chamomile, cloves, coriander (cilantro), oregano, parsley, red clover, rosemary, sage, star anise, thyme.

Selenium

Suggested sources:
Vegetables: Fennel, spinach.
Fruits: Banana.
Other: Barley, Brazil nuts, brown rice (cooked), cashews, eggs, flaxseeds (linseeds), lentils (soaked or sprouted), sunflower seeds.

Zinc

Suggested sources:
Vegetables: Fennel, radish, spinach.
Fruits: Carambola (star fruit), coconut (raw meat), fig (raw).
Herbs: Cloves, thyme.
Other: Almonds, cashews, chia seeds, chickpeas (garbanzo beans), coconut water, hemp seeds, lentils (soaked or sprouted), oats, pine nuts, pumpkin seeds, quinoa.

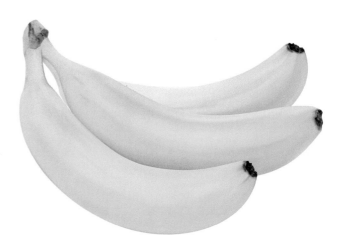

NUTRITION LIST: NUTS, SEEDS, GRAINS, PULSES, FLOWERS

By Karmen Budai, curated by Dr Stephanie Lamb, DVM

This section provides a list of parrot-safe nuts, grains, seeds, legumes and edible flowers and their nutrition profiles. The facts included here are based on animal and human studies, where the information provided is what reports claim as far as the nutrients support body systems. We can use this valuable information to help us provide a diverse diet for our birds.

*Higher levels of vitamins and minerals are marked in bold.

Note that some nuts, grains, seeds and pulses listed within the recipes may not be included in this table.

Nuts	Nutrients	Reported Benefits	Can be soaked?	Does it sprout?	Comments
Almonds	Vitamin E, **calcium**, **magnesium**, **potassium**, zinc, iron, folic acid, manganese, **phosphorus**	Healthy fatty acids and antioxidants supporting heart health; supports brain function; mainly its skin contains probiotic components that help with detoxification and healthy bacterial growth within the gut flora; maintains healthy bones; increases nutrient absorption; almonds' healthy fats improve circulation and maintain skin health.	Yes	Yes	Soaking almonds can increase the bioavailability of fat within the nut and may reduce phytate which is a nutrient that can block absorption of certain minerals.

Nuts	Nutrients	Reported Benefits	Can be soaked?	Does it sprout?	Comments
Brazil Nuts	Vitamin E, **selenium**, **magnesium**, copper, **phosphorus**, **potassium**, manganese, zinc, **calcium**	Very high in selenium; anti-inflammatory; selenium has positive effects on depression, anxiety and mood; **high in protein and fibre**.	No	No	The best food source for selenium. Contains various antioxidants and anti-inflammatory compounds.
Cashews	Vitamin B6, K, copper, **magnesium**, **phosphorus**, **potassium**, zinc, manganese, iron, folate	Improves digestion and nutrient absorption; helps lower levels of inflammation; rich in unsaturated fatty acids and dietary fibre; good source of plant-based protein (27%); improves bone health; supports healthy brain function.	Yes	No	Antioxidant activity increases with roasting but make sure to never salt nuts given to birds.
Chestnut	**Vitamin C**, B6, K, manganese, copper, **folate**, thiamine, **potassium**, riboflavin, **phosphorus**, **magnesium**, pantothenic acid, iron, zinc	Improves digestion; high in fibre; contains antioxidants; boosts bone health; improves brain function; starchy type of nut with higher content of oil and fat.	No	No	Only sweet chestnut (Castanea sativa) is safe for birds and it's the one that is suitable for human consumption and available in supermarkets. These can be eaten raw, boiled, roasted, or ground. Do not confuse these with horse chestnuts (Aesculus hippocastanum) which are not a true chestnut and can be toxic.

Nuts	Nutrients	Reported Benefits	Can be soaked?	Does it sprout?	Comments
Hazelnuts (Filberts)	Vitamin B6, E, K, manganese, copper, thiamine, **magnesium**, **folate**, **phosphorus**, iron, **potassium**, zinc	Contains powerful antioxidants; boosts the brain; great stimulants for healthy metabolism in the body; great sources of "good" fats; vitamin E can contribute to maintaining healthy skin.	Yes	No	The skins have a compound called proanthocyanidins which are a type of antioxidant that can have beneficial effects for the brain and heart.
Macadamia Nuts	Vitamin B6, manganese, thiamine, copper, **magnesium**, iron, **phosphorus**	Fights disease; contains flavonoids that help to prevent cell damage; reduces cholesterol levels; aids in weight loss; contains fibre that supports gut health; strengthens bones; contain omega-9 that benefits the brain function; lower in omega-6s that reduce chronic inflammation.	Yes	No	Although many claim these nuts are needed by certain large species of birds, remember to not overfeed these as they are high in fat and may contribute over time to certain health problems.
Pecan Nuts	Vitamin B6 manganese, copper, thiamine, **magnesium**, iron, zinc, **potassium**, **phosphorus**	Maintains high energy; rich in healthy fats; high in antioxidants; reduces inflammation; contributes to brain function.	Yes	No	A good source of vitamin E which is needed to support a healthy nervous system.

Nuts	Nutrients	Reported Benefits	Can be soaked?	Does it sprout?	Comments
Pine Nuts	**Vitamin K**, B12, E, **magnesium**, **phosphorus**, protein, iron, zinc, thiamine, niacin, **potassium**, riboflavin	Lowers bad cholesterol; supports bone health – vitamin K builds bones better than calcium; rich in carotenoids that support vision; higher levels of magnesium stabilize mood, anxiety and behaviour changes.	No	No	A good training tool due to their small size.
Pistachios	**Vitamin A**, B6, C, E, thiamine, copper, **potassium**, **magnesium**, folate, **calcium**, iron, zinc, niacin	Contains healthy unsaturated fat; helps to improve cholesterol; boosts energy levels, contains a significant amount of the carotenoids that help decrease the risk of disease.	No	No	Offer as a treat in the shell to provide enrichment for the bird. Never offer salted.
Walnuts	Vitamin B6, manganese, copper, **magnesium**, **phosphorus**, **folate**, zinc, iron	Contains the highest amounts of omega-3 fats; supports brain health; improves heart health; walnuts have compounds that burn fat.	Yes	No	Their high omega-3 fatty acid content has anti-inflammatory effects and can be helpful for cardiovascular, skin, and kidney health.

Grains, Seeds, Legumes	Nutrients	Reported Benefits	Can be soaked?	Do they sprout?	Comments
Adzuki Beans	Vitamin B6, **folate**, **phosphorus**, manganese, **potassium**, thiamine, iron, zinc, **calcium**	High mix of protein and fibre; high-antioxidant foods.	Yes	Yes	Best offered in sprouted form.
Alfalfa*	**Vitamin A**, C, **K**, folate, **phosphorus**, magnesium, iron, zinc, copper	Prevents osteoporosis; lowers blood glucose levels; proven high-antioxidant food; cholesterol-lowering food; great supplementary source of vitamin C.	Yes	Yes	*Nutrition data only available for sprouted alfalfa seeds.
Barley	Selenium, **magnesium**, manganese, **phosphorus**, copper, niacin	Good source of important nutrients; high source of soluble fibre found in barley "feeds" probiotic bacteria in the gut; helps with digestion; helps with weight loss; helps control blood sugar levels; contains both omega-3 and omega-6 fatty acids.	Yes	*Yes	*For sprouting look for whole grain barley with hulls intact. Pearled barley won't sprout but it's great for soaking or when cooked.

Grains, Seeds, Legumes	Nutrients	Reported Benefits	Can be soaked?	Do they sprout?	Comments
Broccoli Seeds*	**Vitamin A, C, calcium, iron**	Helps to lower blood pressure; supports bones; detoxifies the body; may improve respiratory function; anti-inflammatory, antioxidant; they contain 10–100 times the sulforaphane found in mature broccoli.	Yes	Yes	*Nutrition data only available for sprouted broccoli seeds.
Buckwheat	Vitamin B6, manganese, **magnesium**, **phosphorus**, niacin, iron, zinc, **folate**, copper, selenium	Packed with nutrients and antioxidants; gluten-free; helps to low cholesterol and inflammation; contains disease-fighting antioxidants; great source of plant-based protein; contains 12 amino acids; high fibre content helps improve digestion.	Yes	Yes	This grain's antioxidant content is higher than most other grains.
Bulgur Wheat	Vitamin B6, **magnesium**, **manganese**, iron, **folate**, phosphorus, zinc	Improves digestion; slows down absorption of sugar; contains high levels of fibre; balances body's pH level; provides important nutrients and antioxidants.	Yes	No	Bulgur is cracked and pre-cooked wheat so not suitable for sprouting.

Grains, Seeds, Legumes	Nutrients	Reported Benefits	Can be soaked?	Do they sprout?	Comments
Chickpeas (garbanzo beans)	Vitamin B6, K, calcium, **magnesium**, zinc, **potassium**, **folate**, copper, **phosphorus**, manganese, iron, thiamine, selenium, pantothenic acid	Great source of plant-based protein; helps control blood sugar levels; provides slow-releasing carbohydrates; high in **fibre** which helps with digestion; great source of folate which is important for new cell production.	Yes	Yes	Although a great source of protein, it does not provide a complete set of proteins, so make sure to pair this with other food items to get a more complete protein profile.
Fenugreek	Vitamin B6, **iron**, manganese, copper, magnesium, phosphorus	Helps reduce internal and external inflammation; improves digestive problems; increases appetite; improves blood sugar levels.	Yes	Yes	This may be helpful in lowering cholesterol and triglycerides in the blood.
Flaxseeds (linseeds)	**Vitamin B1**, B6, K **manganese**, **magnesium**, phosphorus, copper, selenium	Rich source of anti-inflammatory plant-based **omega-3 fatty acids**; great source of dietary fibre and plant-based protein; low in carbs; helps improve digestion, cholesterol and hormone balance; can absorb a lot of liquid; gluten-free; packed with antioxidants.	Yes	No	When soaking flaxseeds it creates a jelly-like substance that can be used as a substitute for eggs when baking your parrot treats. Ground flaxseeds are also great mixed in fresh food. Some of the components in flaxseed meal have been linked to the reduction of certain reproductive cancers in chickens.

Grains, Seeds, Legumes	Nutrients	Reported Benefits	Can be soaked?	Do they sprout?	Comments
Hemp Seeds	**Vitamin E**, manganese, **magnesium**, **phosphorus**, zinc, iron, copper	Controls inflammation and body temperature; works as a natural appetite suppressant; high in insoluble and soluble fibre; good source of **omega-3 and omega-6** fatty acids.	No	No	A complete protein source. It is also high in magnesium which is essential in the pathway involved with normal absorption of calcium from the gut.
Kamut	Vitamin B6, B2, **niacin**, thiamine, folate, manganese, **phosphorus**, **magnesium**, zinc, copper, iron, **calcium**, **folate**	Supports bone health; aids digestive system due to its high **fibre** content; food high in phosphorus can help the body to detox; high in **protein**; manganese and zinc naturally helps to balance hormones; lowers cholesterol.	Yes	Yes	High energy grain.
Lentils (brown, black, green, red, yellow)	Vitamin B5, B6, C, **folate**, manganese, iron, **phosphorus**, copper, thiamine, **potassium**, **magnesium**, zinc, pantothenic acid, selenium	Good source of fibre; helps balance body's PH level; manages blood sugar levels; high in **protein**; improves immunity and digestive health.	Yes	Yes	Split lentils won't sprout. Raw lentils are hard to digest therefore it's recommended to offer them either soaked or sprouted.

Grains, Seeds, Legumes	Nutrients	Reported Benefits	Can be soaked?	Do they sprout?	Comments
Milk Thistle	Not available	Source of antioxidants and has anti-inflammatory properties; natural liver supporter; helps lower high cholesterol levels.	Yes	Yes	Seeds can be brewed in teas too. Great for birds prone to fatty liver disease.
Millet	Vitamin B6, **magnesium**, **folate**, thiamine, iron, **magnesium**, **potassium**, zinc, copper, manganese, calcium, **phosphorus**	Gluten-free; high in **fibre**; source of prebiotic dietary fibre.	Yes	*Yes	*Only millet with hulls will sprout. Offering a full stalk of freshly grown millet can be a great foraging item for a bird.
Mung Beans	Vitamin B1, K, **folate**, manganese, **magnesium**, **phosphorus**, **calcium**, zinc, selenium	Plant-based source of protein; high source of nutrients; high in fibre.	Yes	Yes	One of the safe beans to feed raw–sprouted or soaked.

Grains, Seeds, Legumes	Nutrients	Reported Benefits	Can be soaked?	Do they sprout?	Comments
Oat Groats	Vitamin B5, **phosphorus**, selenium, manganese, **magnesium**, iron, zinc, copper	High **fibre** food; helps lower cholesterol; helps improve digestion; contains Beta-glucans which are known to enhance immune function by fighting bacterial infection and lowering inflammation; contains higher source of protein compared to most grains.	Yes	*Yes	*For sprouting must use unhulled oats so-called "whole oats".
Peas (whole dried or split)	**Vitamin A**, iron, calcium, **potassium**	Great source of protein and dietary fibre.	Yes*	Yes**	*Split peas are great for soaking. ** Only whole peas will sprout.
Quinoa (red, black, white)	Vitamin B6, E, manganese, **magnesium**, iron, **phosphorus**, **folate**, iron, copper, thiamine, selenium, riboflavin, zinc, **potassium**, **calcium**	Gluten-free; a complete protein source and has a complete profile of all 20 amino acids, including the nine essential amino acids; great source of antioxidants and high in healthy fats; keeps the gut healthy; supports bone health; great source of fibre.	Yes	Yes	A great protein source that is readily accepted by even the smallest of birds due to its small size. Rinse thoroughly to remove saponin.

Grains, Seeds, Legumes	Nutrients	Reported Benefits	Can be soaked?	Do they sprout?	Comments
Radish Seeds*	Vitamin A, B6, C, folate, calcium, potassium, **phosphorus**, magnesium	Promotes digestive health; lowers blood pressure; detoxifies the liver; strengthens the bones; improves cardiovascular health.	Yes	Yes	*Nutrition data only available for sprouted radish seeds.
Rye	Vitamin E, folate, **phosphorus**, **potassium**, **magnesium**, selenium, sodium, zinc, calcium	Powerhouse of antioxidants, phytonutrients; good source of fibre; maintains digestive health.	Yes	Yes	Watch for ergot mould.
Sesame Seeds	Vitamin B6, copper, manganese, **calcium**, **magnesium**, iron, **phosphorus**, zinc, thiamine	Contains up to 60% oil and 20% protein; helps to lower cholesterol levels and balance hormone levels; high in fibre; good source of essential fatty acids needed for the absorption of fat-soluble vitamins A, D, E and K.	Yes	Yes	A good source of calcium. Must use unhulled sesame seeds for sprouting.

What is fibre?

Fibre plays an important role not only in the human diet but in a bird's diet too. Offering high fibre food will help to maintain your bird's digestive system so it functions properly.

Grains, Seeds, Legumes	Nutrients	Reported Benefits	Can be soaked?	Do they sprout?	Comments
Sunflower Seeds	**Vitamin E**, B6, B3, copper, **thiamine**, **phosphorus**, manganese, **selenium**, **magnesium**, **folate**, iron, zinc, **potassium**	High in omega-6 fatty acids; excellent source of fibre; vitamin E helps to reduce body-wide inflammation; rich in antioxidants and anti-inflammatory compounds.	Yes	Yes	Sunflower seeds have a very high oil content. Very nutritious when soaked or sprouted. Make sure to provide in moderation as birds love these. Hulled or unhulled, may be soaked and sprouted.
Teff	Vitamin B2, B6, thiamine, niacin, manganese, **magnesium**, **phosphorus**, iron, copper, zinc, **calcium**, **potassium**, **sodium**	Gluten-free grain; helps naturally balance hormone levels; stimulates digestion; boosts immune system; strengthens bones; high in fibre and plant-based protein; iron in teff increases digestion oxygenation to important organs.	Yes	Yes	High in the amino acid lysine, which is deficient in traditional seed diets.
Wheat Berries	Vitamin B6, manganese, **selenium**, thiamine, **phosphorus**, **magnesium**, niacin, folate, zinc	Nutrient-dense food; great source of fibre which is beneficial for digestive system and has been shown to lower cholesterol levels; regulates blood sugar levels; aids in weight loss; strengthens bones.	Yes	Yes	Can be added to soil and grown into wheatgrass.

EDIBLE FLOWERS

Flowers, buds and nectar have been part of a diverse diet for many species in their natural habitat. So why not include them in your bird's diet. In addition to their nutritional value, flowers can provide important mental stimulation and many parrots simply enjoy tearing them apart. Here is a list of the most common edible flowers which can be offered to your flock daily, either fresh or dried, together with their fresh food. Most of the listed edible flowers can be found in your local supermarket or speciality online food stores, alternatively you can check organic local farms or grow your own.

*Safety – when buying flowers from your supermarket ensure they are stored within the food section and labelled as **edible** and <u>suitable for human consumption</u>. Never give your bird flowers from florists, garden centres or nurseries as those would have been sprayed with pesticides and are only suitable for decorative purposes. Avoid picking any flowers that grow near busy roads as those would be exposed to dust, fumes and chemicals used for spraying the side of the roads to eliminate weeds. Always check that the flower is on a parrot-safe list.*

PARROT-SAFE EDIBLE FLOWERS

Borage Blossoms *(Borago officinalis)*

Nutrients: vitamin A, C, folate, niacin, riboflavin, pyridoxine, potassium, magnesium, calcium, iron.
Benefits: low-calorie culinary herb; contains omega-6 fatty acid that plays a vital role in the restoration of joint health, immunity and healthy skin; is high in vitamin C; is one of the moderate sources of B-complex vitamins. They can also have a diuretic effect. Not to be consumed in large quantities. May be beneficial for adjunctive therapy for certain diseases but consultation with a veterinarian is recommended.
Taste: has light cucumber taste.

Photo by Yoksel Yok

Calendula *(Calendula officinalis)*

Benefits: has powerful healing effects internally and externally; has strong anti-inflammatory properties via powerful flavonoid; helps speed up healing of wounds; contains antimicrobial and antiviral components; has muscle relaxing abilities. Ranges in colour from golden yellow to deep orange.
Taste: has mild sweetly vegetal to slightly bitter flavour.

Chamomile *(Matricaria recutita)*

Benefits: commonly used for improving inflammatory conditions, muscle spasms, skin disorders, wounds, gastrointestinal disorders, fighting skin irritations and helping to ease anxiety; high source of antioxidants; it's a powerful digestive relaxant; has antimicrobial properties and helps to fight infections.
Taste: has soft, floral taste with a mild apple flavour.

Photo by Rebecca Asryan

Chrysthanthemum

Nutrients: vitamin A, B6, K, thiamine, riboflavin, calcium, magnesium, phosphorus, potassium, sodium, iron.
Benefits: helps to reduce inflammation and calm nerves; possesses powerful antioxidants and promotes relaxation.
Taste: has mild, slightly sweet flowery taste.

Clover Flowers *(Trifolium)*

Nutrients: vitamin C, calcium, magnesium, niacin, phosphorus, potassium, thiamine.
Benefits: acts like a natural diuretic; helps to improve immune function; may help fight inflammation, infections and hormonal imbalances; can help treat coughs and respiratory infections; rich source of isoflavones-compounds acting as phytoestrogens; has blood-thinning abilities.
Taste: flowers have sweet taste.
Note – Can contribute to reproductive problems in certain animals due to containing isoflavones. Use with the guidance of a veterinarian in hormonal animals.

Cornflowers *(Centaurea cyanus)*

Photo by Marek Pewnicki

Benefits: effective for yeast infections, constipation, chest congestion, liver and gallbladder disorders.
Taste: the flowers have no fragrance and they have a sweet-to-spicy clove-like flavour.

Dahlia

Benefits: petals were used in the past for treating rashes and cracks in the skin.
Comes in varying shades of pink, white, orange, red, purple yellow.
Taste: flavours range from water chestnut to spicy apple.

Dandelion Flowers *(Taraxacum oficinale)*

Nutrients: vitamin A, B12, potassium.
Benefits: has a higher level of polyphenols than the leaves or roots which help in the prevention of cardiovascular disease; good source of antioxidants; has anti-inflammatory properties. Leaves are also safe to feed and are packed with nutrition. Also found to have benefits for liver function.
Taste: has slight bitter taste.

Photo by Dmitry Tulupov

Elderflower

Benefits: packed with antioxidants, has diuretic properties. Only flowers and berries are safe to feed and only black elderberries can be eaten raw.
Taste: has fruity and slightly floral with subtle pear flavour.

Photo by Corina Rainer

Hibiscus Flower *(Hibiscus rosa-sinensis)*

Benefits: mainly offered as tea; good source of vitamin C which boosts immune system; helps to lower blood pressure; full of antioxidants.
Taste: has fruity, citrus like flavour.
Note – Can negatively affect certain meds so always consult with your vet. Extremely high doses of hibiscus tea are damaging to the liver.

Honeysuckle *(Japanese Lonicera japonica)*

Benefits: has anti-inflammatory properties; flower buds are beneficial in treating digestion problems; honeysuckle iced tea offers refreshment during hot summer days; helps with nausea; as an infusion can be used to treat upper respiratory tract infections.
Safety: only this type of honeysuckle flower is edible and safe for birds. Don't offer the berries or the vines as these are toxic, flowers only!
Taste: has a strong sweet flavour and birds just love the honeysuckle nectar.

Lavender (*Lavandula officinalis*)

Nutrients: vitamin A, calcium, iron.
Benefits: it is known for its calming effects as it has positive effects on mood, stress, anxiety; its antioxidants may contribute to wound healing; aids respiratory issues. Lavender tea can help ease anxiety for any stressed bird. May interfere with medications so consult your vet before offering it to your pet bird.
Taste: it's a fragrant flower with strong flavour.

Photo by Thomas Vogel

Lilac (*Syringa vulgaris*)

Benefits: provide a calming effect that eases anxiety.
Taste: has strong floral fragrance and slightly bitter citrusy flavour.

Photo by Adriana Saraceanu

Nasturtiums (*Tropaeolum majos*)

Nutrients: vitamin C, potassium, phosphorus, magnesium, calcium, manganese, copper, zinc and iron.
Benefits: good source of vitamin C; high in antioxidants; may have natural anti-inflammatory and antibacterial effects; contains trace elements and bioactive compounds that can help support the immune, respiratory and digestive systems.
Taste: has a peppery, watercress-like flavour. Leaves can also be fed.

Photo by Maylee

Pansies (*Viola tricolor var. hortensis*)

Benefits: rich in antioxidants; infusions are effective for skin inflammation; has diuretic and anti-inflammatory properties; improves blood circulation.
Taste: they have a mild, fresh and lightly floral flavour.

Photo by Jorge Munoz

Rose Petals *(Rosa species)*

Nutrients: vitamin C, iron, calcium.
Here are some of the safe roses where the petals can be offered to our birds: Rosa gallica, Rosa xdamascena, Rosa rugosa, Flower carpet rose, Double Delight, Mirandy roses, Tiffany roses variety.
Benefits: reported to possess laxative/purgative, antibacterial and antimicrobial activities; certain compounds in roses promote relaxation.
Taste: delicate aromatic and slight fruity flavour.

Photo by Rebecca Matthews

Sunflower *(Helianthus)*

Nutritional data provided are for the sunflower seeds
Nutrients: vitamin E, B1, B5, B6, copper, niacin, magnesium, selenium.
Benefits: loaded with nutrients; high in vitamin E which helps to reduce inflammation; helps to lower cholesterol; balances blood sugar levels; high in fibre; high in omega-6 (too much omega-6 and not enough omega-3 leads to inflammation and health problems).
Great for foraging as the flower offers one of the bird's most favourite snack – seeds.

Photo by Serrah Galos

Vegetable flowers
Butterblossom squash flowers, okra, pumpkin, runner bean flowers, zucchini flowers.

Herb flowers
Anise, basil, bee balm, chives, coriander (cilantro), dill, fennel, garlic, oregano, rosemary, thyme.

Tree flowers
Apple, bottlebrush, eucalyptus, grapefruit, kumquat, lemon, lime, melaleuca, orange, plum.

KEEPING YOUR PARROT'S GUT BACTERIA IN BALANCE

By Dr Jamie Abete, DVM

We have long known that what we eat affects the bacteria that live in our digestive tracts, and the same is likely true for our feathered companions. There have been several studies in the last two decades on the species of bacteria that inhabit both wild and captive parrots' gut, but not nearly as many on what specific factors allow a parrot's beneficial gut microbe species to flourish while keeping potentially harmful bacteria species in check. Extrapolating from studies carried out on other species we can see that fibre appears to be critically important in keeping good bacteria numbers high, preventing harmful bacteria from over-replicating.

Evidence suggests that a diet under 15% fibre results in higher levels of harmful bacteria in the intestinal tract, which can lead to increased risk of illness.[3] Low fibre diets and diets containing purified prebiotic fibres, like the fibres commonly found in processed foods, have been shown to cause damage to the colon lining by allowing pathogenic bacteria to replicate uninhibited by more desired bacteria species.[3] More studies are needed that directly focus on parrot species to verify the exact amount of fibre required to keep healthy gut flora at appropriate levels. There are quite a number of studies focusing on chickens' intestinal flora, but parrots differ significantly from many other bird species as they do not have ceca (an appendage off the large intestine that ferments some carbohydrates and helps reabsorb water), so it is unclear how useful these studies are in understanding parrot gut health.[8] It is likely that different parrot species have differing fibre requirements, as they appear to have different intestinal microbiotia even when kept in very similar environments and are given nearly identical resources.[4]

Many parrot supplements and formulated diets include the probiotic *Latobacillus*, but supplementation alone has not been shown to prevent more pathogenic bacteria from inhabiting parrots' intestinal tracts.[4] In some species *Lactobacillus* supplementation has been shown to help regulate the immune system and improve growth through increasing absorption of proteins and essential minerals, but these findings have yet to be proven in parrots.[7] There is some evidence that supplementing *Lactobacillus* may actually decrease the diversity of a parrot's intestinal microbiome, but we do not yet know the significance of this finding.[4] Wild parrots have been shown to have different intestinal bacteria populations than captive parrots, with significantly less diversity in bacterial species present.[9] We don't know at this time if we should be looking to supplement captive parrots with probiotic species more common in healthy captive parrots or healthy wild parrots to achieve optimal health. It is possible that the intestinal bacteria differences seen in captive versus wild birds is due to diet, but it may also be due to other environmental factors or selection throughout generations of captive bred birds.

The best way to make sure your bird has enough fibre in their diet is to feed a diet rich in whole fresh foods. Plants are typically rich in fibre, especially green vegetables. Many fruits are high in fibre, especially if eaten with the skin. Some grains are also rich in fibre, like quinoa, oats and brown rice. It can be next to impossible to tell how much dietary fibre most formulated parrot diets have unless they have it listed on the label. Most formulated pellet diets on the market have anywhere from 3–5% crude fibre, which is not the same as dietary fibre. Crude fibre refers to the residue (cellulose and lignin) left over after the product is treated with acid and alkali. There is no direct formula to tell how much dietary fibre (the components of a plant that are resistant to normal digestion) a food contains by the amount of crude fibre listed, so unless a product has dietary fibre posted you cannot tell how much is present.[2]

More research is needed to determine the importance of many types of gut flora in parrots. There are a number of probiotic supplements on the market that primarily focus on providing *Lactobacillus* and *Bifidobacterium* species, which are known to be nonpathogenic and potentially helpful, particularly after antibiotic use, illness or other stressful life event.[6] We know that most of a parrot's gut flora should be gram-positive bacteria, and very little (under 10%) gram-negative bacteria, so supplementing with beneficial gram-positive bacteria should help shift away from more pathogenic gram-negative bacterial strains. [1, 5] Whether you are supplementing your parrot with a probiotic after an illness or preventatively, feeding a nutritionally sound diet rich in plant derived-fibre should help the probiotic be as effective as possible and keep native gut flora healthy.

Works Cited:

[1] Allegretti, L., et al. "Isolation and Molecular Identification of Lactic Acid Bacteria and Bifidobacterium Spp. from Faeces of the Blue-Fronted Amazon Parrot in Brazil." *Beneficial Microbes*, vol. 5, no. 4, 2014, pp. 497–503., doi:10.3920/bm2013.0082.

[2] "Carbohydrates and Fiber." *Recommended Dietary Allowances*, National Academy Press, 1989, p. 39.

[3] Desai, Mahesh S., et al. "A Dietary Fiber-Deprived Gut Microbiota Degrades the Colonic Mucus Barrier and Enhances Pathogen Susceptibility." Cell, vol. 167, no. 5, 2016., doi:10.1016/j.cell.2016.10.043.

[4] Liu, Hongyi, et al. "Characterization and Comparison of Gut Microbiomes in Nine Species of Parrots in Captivity." *Symbiosis*, vol. 78, no. 3, 2019, pp. 241–250., doi:10.1007/s13199-019-00613-7.

[5] Sakas, Peter S., and Louise Bauck. *Essentials of Avian Medicine: a Guide for Practitioners*. American Animal Hospital Association Press, 2002.

[6] Smith, Jeanne Marie. "A Review of Avian Probiotics." *Journal of Avian Medicine and Surgery*, vol. 28, no. 2, 2014, pp. 87–94., doi:10.1647/2012-031.

[7] Valeriano, V.D.V., et al. "Probiotic Roles Of Lactobacillus sp. in Swine: Insights from Gut Microbiota." *Journal of Applied Microbiology*, vol. 122, no. 3, 2017, pp. 554–567., doi:10.1111/jam.13364.

[8] Waite, David W., and Michael W. Taylor. "Exploring the Avian Gut Microbiota: Current Trends and Future Directions." *Frontiers in Microbiology*, vol. 6, 2015., doi:10.3389/fmicb.2015.00673.

[9] Xenoulis, Panagiotis G., et al. "Molecular Characterization of the Cloacal Microbiota of Wild and Captive Parrots." *Veterinary Microbiology*, vol. 146, no. 3–4, 2010, pp. 320–325., doi:10.1016/j.vetmic.2010.05.024.

SOAKING AND SPROUTING FOR YOUR PARROT

SOAKING

What is soaking and why should you include it in your bird's diet? Soaking is a simple process where you soak the item in cool water for a certain period of time. Soaking nuts, seeds, legumes and grains will help to remove the "anti-nutrients" like phytic acids and enzyme inhibitors that protect the seed, nut or grain from germination, and will make the essential vitamins and minerals more available and easier for your pet bird to digest. If offering an item in its dry form, the phytic acid binds to minerals like iron, zinc and calcium in the gastrointestinal tract and cannot be absorbed in the intestine which can lead to mineral deficiencies. Soaking activates the seed which is then ready for germination.

Have you ever tried soaked nuts? The taste is completely different to its dry counterpart; they become softer with a more buttery taste – raw. Including soaked seeds, grains, pulses and nuts in your bird's diet is as important as offering fresh vegetables and fruits and it should form at least 20% of their diet.

The guide opposite will help you with the soaking and sprouting times for some of the most commonly used grains, seeds, legumes and nuts.

Step 1: Always make sure you wash the item first before leaving it to soak.

Step 2: Place the item in a bowl and cover it with cool water so it is completely submerged in the water. Leave it to soak as long as required.

Step 3: After soaking, rinse well in cool water and strain. Then it is ready to be added into your bird's fresh food.

Tip: Soaking will increase, if not double, the size of an item, so ensure you put enough water in a bowl. Soak at room temperature. **Never use hot water.**

ITEM	SOAK TIME	SPROUT TIME
Grains		
Amaranth	2–4 hours	1–1.5 days
Barley (Pearl Barley won't sprout)	6–8 hours	2 days
Buckwheat	15 minutes	1–2 days
Field Corn	8–14 hours	2+ days
Kamut	8–14 hours	1–1.5 days
Millet	8 hours	2–3 days
Oat Groats	8–14 hours	1–1.5 days
Quinoa (white, red, black)	2 hours	1–2 days
Rye	8–14 hours	1–1.5 days
Spelt	8–14 hours	1–1.5 days
Teff	2 hours	1 day
Wheat	7 hours	2–3 days
Legumes		
Adzuki Beans	8 hours	3–5 days
Alfalfa	4–14 hours	1–1.5 days
Chickpeas (Garbanzo Beans)	12 hours	12 hours
Clover	4–14 hours	1–1.5 days
Lentils (brown/green/red)	8 hours	12 hours
Mung Beans	1 day	2–5 days
Peas (whole)	12 hours	2–3 days
Nuts & Seeds		
Almonds (hulled)	8–12 hours	12 hours
Cashew	2.5 hours	N/A
Coriander Seeds	8 hours	N/A
Fenugreek Seeds	8 hours	2–3 days
Flaxseeds (linseeds)	8 hours	N/A
Pecans	4–6 hours	N/A
Poppy Seeds	8 hours	1–2 days
Pumpkin Seeds (Pepitas)	6–8 hours	1–2 days
Radish Seeds	8 hours	2–3 days
Sesame Seeds	8 hours	1–2 days
Sunflower Seeds	2 hours	2–3 days
Walnuts	4 hours	N/A

SPROUTING

When sprouting the seeds, grains and legumes for your bird you will need to start with the soaking process first before anything can start to sprout.

Day 1: Once you have completed the above soaking process, place the soaked items into a sprouting jar and cover with a mesh lid to allow good air flow. Make sure any excess water can be drained out during the sprouting process.

Day 2: Rinse well under cool water and place the sprouts in a GSE (Grapefruit Seed Extract) water mixture for about five minutes then strain without rinsing. Repeat this step daily – morning and evening – until your sprouts are ready. When you see tiny tails coming out, they are ready to be harvested, so rinse one final time and strain thoroughly before serving.

Tip: Using specific sprouting jars can be the best way for those new to sprouting as they can easily be inverted and propped at an angle to drain any excess water properly during the sprouting, decreasing chances of getting mouldy sprouts. GSE helps to deter any microbial growth, rinsing sprouts in only cool water won't do the job.

Storing sprouts and soaked food

Sprouts and soaked food should be transferred into a plastic container, sealed tightly and stored in the refrigerator for up to a maximum of three days. Ensure the sprouts have drained completely before storing them, you can always place a paper towel on top to soak up any remaining moisture. Always check for any sour smell or mould before serving to your pet bird. If unsure dispose immediately, as any off items may cause illness.

Safety Tip: Never sprout or soak soup type beans as these can't be fed raw to your pet bird. Soup beans contain a compound called lectin which is toxic, and it can only be removed with cooking. The safest beans to be offered raw (sprouted or soaked) are mung and adzuki beans.

Mouldy sprouts or root hair?

Sprouting at home is an easy and cheap way of providing nutritious greens for your flock but sometimes those new to sprouting encounter a problem that discourages them from sprouting again – the mould! Or is that really a mould on my sprouts?

Mould

Root Hair

It can often be confusing to spot the difference between a mouldy batch of sprouts and a healthy one that has these tiny feather-like roots. But it is always worth checking this before serving it to your pet bird. Here are the most common signs to look out for.

Root hair signs (Cilia Hairs)
> They are formed from two to three days and are always fine and white

> Your sprouts smell like a healthy plant and not like wet soil

> They grow thicker as the sprout grows

> They stick to the root and break easily

> They are only formed on the root itself and never formed on stem or leaves

> They will disappear after rinsing

The most common sprouts with root hair are: broccoli, buckwheat, radish, sunflower, barley, wheat.

Mould signs
> Looks like tiny cobwebs spread around clusters of seeds

> Greyish colour

> Strong odour that will not disappear after rinsing

> Feels slimy

What causes mould?
> Sprouter with poor air circulation

> Water is not draining well from the sprouter

> High humidity in the room you keep your sprouts in

> Dirty sprouter

> Rinsing with warm water or not rinsing at least twice a day

Tip: During hot summer days you can always place your sprouter in the fridge, but it will take a bit longer for your sprouts to come out than if sprouted at the room temperature.

HOW TO GROW MICROGREENS

Microgreens are young vegetable greens that despite their small size are packed with higher nutrient levels than their larger counterparts and have been linked to providing support to the immune system. Some often confuse them with sprouts. So what is the difference? Microgreens germinate in soil, require sunlight to grow and are usually harvested between 7–14 days and have reached one to three inches in height. Sprouts on the other hand germinate after soaking in water and grow in a sprouting jar for up to five days before being harvested.

Microgreens have unique and intense flavours depending on the variety and are an absolutely delicious addition in fresh salads and mashes for your bird. They can also provide a nice textural contrast and make your bird's meal a fine dining experience.

Mature vegetables can never be a replacement for providing your bird with the necessary fibre, but microgreens can fill in the gap in your bird's diet by providing additional nutrients.

Which microgreens are safe for your bird?

The most common are amaranth, basil, beets, broccoli, buckwheat, cabbage, cauliflower, celery, chard, chia, coriander (cilantro), cress, daikon radish, dill, fennel, fenugreek, kale, kohlrabi, lemon balm, lettuce, mustard, pak choi, parsley, pea shoots, radish, red amaranth, red basil, red chard, rocket (arugula), sage, spinach, sunflower shoots, sweetcorn shoots, Swiss chard, Thai basil, thyme, watercress.

SPROUT
2-5 days

MICROGREEN
7-14 days

What you need to grow your own microgreens

1. Soil and two planting trays
(as an alternative to soil you could use special fibre mats on which the seeds can root)
2. Seeds
3. Spray bottle

It is simple and anyone can grow them at home to produce trays of nutritious greens for your everyday fresh chop.

Step 1: First buy an appropriate soil that is suitable to grow microgreens in, preferably organic. Then fill the tray and spread the soil to make it level by using your hands, press down to make a firm bed. Make sure the tray has a few drainage holes. Gently moisten the soil with cool water.

Step 2: Spread the seeds across the tray evenly. Spray with cool water and make sure they are damp. Place the second tray on top which will keep them in dark during the germination process and help to force the roots to grow downwards. Keep the tray in a dark warm place. You will then need to moisten the seeds once or twice per day until they have finished germination.

Step 3: After three to five days you will notice the sprouts start growing. The time may vary as it depends on the type of seeds you will be growing as they all germinate at different times. At this stage you can remove the top tray and place them in a warm area that has natural sunlight. Continue to spray daily until they are ready to be trimmed and added to your bird's fresh food.

TIP: When buying the seeds always look for organic or chemically untreated seeds and same applies when choosing the right soil.

Recipes

CHOPS AND MASHES

Feeding fresh food to your bird should be considered as a main part of a healthy diet together with plenty of sprouted seeds and grains, soaked seeds and nuts. This will offer the best possible nutrition in the most natural form. Chops and mashes are easy to make and will create a great foraging opportunity for your bird.

Power Mash

Vegetables
½ green bell pepper, chopped
2 tbsp baby cucumbers, finely chopped
½ carrot, peeled, grated
½ cup green squash, diced small
Sprig of tenderstem broccoli, to garnish

Dry Items
1 tbsp organic barley flakes
1 tbsp pumpkin seeds (pepitas)
2 tsp Polly's avian herbal tea

Soaked
1 tsp buckwheat
1 tbsp alfalfa seeds
1 tbsp barley grain
1 tbsp fenugreek seeds
1 tbsp wheat grain
1 tbsp almonds, roughly chopped
1 tbsp cashews
1 tbsp pecan nuts

Sprouted
1 tbsp adzuki beans
1 tbsp mung beans
1 tbsp milk thistle seeds

> Prepare the soaked and sprouted ingredients in advance. Chop all the vegetables as suggested and place them in your bird's bowl.
> Add the dry, soaked and sprouted items and toss gently. Finish it off with a small sprig of broccoli in the middle.

Photo by David Vives

Small Mash

Vegetables and Herbs

1 cup black cabbage, finely sliced

½ carrot, finely chopped

½ cup courgette (zucchini), small diced

¼ cup cucumber, finely chopped

¼ yellow bell pepper, finely chopped

1 tbsp fresh coriander, finely chopped

1 tbsp salad cress microgreens

1 radish, grated, to garnish

Soaked

1 tbsp buckwheat

1 tbsp barley grain

1 tbsp oat groats

1 tbsp sesame seeds

1 tbsp pecans, chopped

1 tbsp cashews, chopped

Sprouted

1 tbsp broccoli seeds

1 tbsp alfalfa seeds

1 tsp radish seeds, to garnish

> Prepare the soaked and sprouted ingredients in advance. Chop all the vegetables and herbs as suggested and place them in your bird's bowl. Add all the soaked and sprouted items and toss gently.

> Garnish with the grated radish and sprinkle with the sprouted radish seeds.

Fact: Even our smallest beaks can be fed fresh food.

Tip: For smaller birds such as budgerigars, cockatiels and similar sized species you can chop the veggies by using a food processor.

Sweet Potato Falafel and Salad

Falafel

½ sweet potato, steamed

1 tbsp hemp seeds

1 tbsp soaked almonds and walnuts, finely chopped

1 tsp flaxseeds (linseeds)

1 tsp sesame seeds

1 tbsp raw or cooked sweetcorn (NOT from a tin)

Salad

½ cup red chicory, sliced

½ small beetroot, diced

½ cup butternut squash, diced

½ carrot, chopped

1 radish, thinly sliced

1 tbsp pomegranate seeds

1 tbsp fennel, finely chopped

1 sprig of fresh parsley, finely chopped

> **For the falafel:** first steam the sweet potato until soft. In a bowl, mash up the sweet potato with a fork and mix well with all the listed ingredients, and form into small balls.

> **For the salad:** chop all the vegetables and herbs as suggested and place them in a bowl, toss gently.

> Place the ready-made falafels on top of the salad.

Kale Chop

Vegetables and Herbs

Handful of kale,
  chopped
4 radishes, chopped
¼ kohlrabi, diced
¼ cup courgette
  (zucchini), diced
¼ cup cauliflower,
  chopped
1 tbsp raw peas
1 tbsp parsley, finely
  chopped
1 tbsp basil, finely
  chopped
Variety of edible
  flowers, to garnish

Dry Items

1 tsp ground flaxseeds
  (linseeds)
1 tsp organic oregano
1 tbsp barley flakes
1 tbsp Brazil nuts,
  roughly chopped
4 dried mini chilli
  peppers, to garnish

Soaked

1 tbsp quinoa
1 tbsp buckwheat

> Prepare the soaked ingredients in advance. Chop all the vegetables and herbs as suggested and place them in your bird's bowl. Then add all the soaked ingredients and toss gently.

> Garnish with the dry chilli peppers and edible flowers.

Butternut Squash Platter

Vegetables and Herbs

1 thick slice of
  butternut squash, as
  base (keep the seeds)
¼ cup fresh dandelion
  leaves, chopped
½ cup mix of yellow and
  orange bell pepper,
  chopped
¼ cup white chicory,
  finely chopped
1 sprig of broccoli,
  chopped
2 baby sweetcorn,
  sliced
½ small carrot, grated

3 star anise, whole, to
  garnish
1 Physalis, to garnish
Apple blossoms
  (edible flowers)*, to
  garnish (to be fed in
  moderation)
Nasturtium (edible
  flowers)*, to garnish

Sprouted

1 tbsp milk thistle seeds
1 tbsp rye grain
1 tbsp hemp seeds
1 tsp white sesame
  seeds (hulled)

❯ Prepare the sprouted ingredients in advance. Cut a thick slice (approximately 2 cm) of the butternut squash and place it at the bottom of a bowl or on a plate. Remember to set the seeds on one side.

❯ **For the filling:** chop all the remaining vegetables as suggested and combine them with sprouts, toss gently. Place this filling on the butternut squash base.

❯ Garnish with a variety of edible flowers, the star anise and sprinkle with the raw butternut squash seeds.

Baby Cucumber Tower

Vegetables and Herbs

1 baby cucumber, sliced sideways – 4 pieces needed

2 baby sweetcorn, sliced

1 baby orange bell pepper

½ cup black cabbage, chopped

½ cup pak choi (bok choy), chopped

2 tbsp raw butternut squash, grated

5 sugar snap peas, chopped

1 tbsp raw green peas

1 tbsp fresh parsley, finely chopped

1 sprig of fresh thyme, chopped

1 tbsp dill, chopped

1 sprig of dill, to garnish

2 tbsp salad cress microgreens, to garnish

Dry Items

1 tbsp whole almonds

1 tbsp coconut flakes (unsweetened)

1 tsp ground flaxseeds (linseeds)

1 tsp Polly's avian herbal tea

Soaked

1 tbsp red and brown lentils

1 tbsp barley grain

1 tbsp rye grain

❯ First prepare the soaked ingredients in advance. Then slice the cucumber sideways into four long pieces and lay them in a bowl or on a plate to create a square shape.

❯ Chop all the vegetables and herbs as instructed (except the microgreens), place them in a separate bowl and carefully add the dry and soaked ingredients. Mix gently.

❯ Using a spoon, transfer the mix into the prepared bowl or plate, making sure to place the ingredients inside the cucumber square. Garnish with the microgreens and a fresh sprig of dill.

The Moroccan Way Chop

Vegetables and Herbs

¼ courgette (zucchini)
 – use a spiraliser

1 tbsp raw peas

1 tbsp sweetcorn – raw
 or cooked (NOT from
 a tin)

1 Scotch bonnet chilli
 pepper, chopped

¼ sweet potato,
 steamed, mashed

1 slice of swede
 (rutabaga) steamed,
 mashed

1 sprig of fresh
 coriander, finely
 chopped

Dry Items

1 tbsp Polly's avian
 herbal tea

1 tsp dry oregano

Soaked

1 tbsp red and brown
 lentils

2 tbsp walnuts,
 almonds, pumpkin
 seeds (pepitas),
 cashews – chopped

Sprouted

1 tbsp mung beans

1 tbsp red clover seeds

1 tbsp chickpeas
 (garbanzo beans)

> Prepare the soaked and sprouted ingredients in advance. To make the topping balls, cut the sweet potato and swede into small cubes, place them into a steamer basket and cover. Remove once tender, drain, and let the cubes cool. Mash them up with a fork then add the finely chopped coriander and soaked lentils. Form small balls and leave aside.

> Using a spiraliser or similar attachment, cut the courgette into strips. Place the strips into a bowl and mix in the remaining vegetables, the soaked and sprouted ingredients, followed by the dry items. Toss gently. Sprinkle with avian herbal tea and finish by placing the topping balls on top of the chop.

Green Chop on Watercress Bed

Vegetables and Herbs
Handful of watercress
½ cup rainbow chard, chopped
1 Scotch bonnet chilli pepper, chopped
1 green chilli pepper, chopped
¼ cup white and red radish, finely chopped
¼ cup fennel, chopped
1 small beetroot, diced
¼ cup raw pumpkin, chopped (not from a tin)
1 sprig of fresh thyme, chopped
1 sprig of fresh coriander, chopped
2 okras, sliced, to garnish
¼ red bell pepper, sliced, to garnish

Dry Items
1 tbsp walnuts, crushed
1 tsp ground flaxseeds (linseeds)
1 tbsp organic chamomile

Soaked
1 tsp hulled millet
1 tsp teff
1 tsp red quinoa

Sprouted
1 tbsp barley grain
1 tbsp rye grain
1 tbsp adzuki beans

> Prepare the soaked and sprouted ingredients in advance. Chop all the vegetables and herbs as suggested except the watercress, then start adding all the dry, soaked and sprouted ingredients. Lay the watercress on the bottom of a bowl and place the chop mix on top. Then garnish with slices of okra and red bell pepper. I used a food-grade bamboo boat dish to serve in and Polly absolutely loved shredding it to pieces. Great for fussy beaks as it can encourage them to try new food.

Summer Chop

Vegetables and Herbs
½ cup cauliflower, chopped
½ yellow bell pepper, chopped
½ cup chard, sliced
¼ cup courgette (zucchini), diced
1 tbsp raw peas
1 tbsp raw sweetcorn
4 green beans, chopped
½ cup pumpkin, shavings
½ cup pak choi (bok choy), sliced
1 tbsp celeriac, diced
1 sprig of fresh thyme, chopped

Dry Items
1 tbsp shelled hemp seeds
1 tsp white hulled sesame seeds
1 tbsp Polly's avian herbal tea

Soaked
1 tbsp black sesame seeds
1 tbsp coriander seeds
1 tbsp spelt grain
1 tbsp sunflower seeds

> First prepare the soaked ingredients in advance. Then chop all the vegetables and herbs as suggested and place them in a bowl. Add all the dry and soaked items, toss gently and the meal is ready to be served.

Choi Sum Chop

Vegetables
1 cup choi sum, thinly chopped
1 cup yellow marrow squash, diced
½ cup white chicory, chopped
1 tbsp raw sweetcorn
1 tbsp raw peas
Handful of spinach, chopped
½ orange bell pepper, chopped
½ cup cress microgreens

Dry Items
1 tsp ground flaxseeds (linseeds)
1 tbsp coconut flakes (unsweetened)

Soaked
1 tbsp split yellow peas
1 tsp amaranth
1 tbsp almonds, to garnish

Sprouted
1 tbsp mung beans
1 tbsp chickpeas (garbanzo beans)
1 tbsp red lentils

> Prepare the soaked and sprouted ingredients in advance. Chop all the vegetables as suggested and place them in a bowl.
> Add the dry, soaked and sprouted ingredients, toss gently and garnish with the whole soaked almonds. You may want to reduce the number of almonds if feeding smaller birds where one almond is plenty for them.

Flower Mash

Vegetables and Herbs

½ red bell pepper, thinly sliced

1 small carrot, chopped

5 green beans, chopped

2 sprigs of baby broccoli, chopped

¼ cup cauliflower, finely chopped

1 tbsp fresh basil, finely chopped

1 sprig of fresh thyme, chopped

Handful of Tagetes (edible flowers), to garnish

Soaked

1 tbsp green lentils

1 tbsp hulled millet

1 tbsp black sesame seeds, to garnish

Sprouted

1 tbsp brown mustard seeds

1 tbsp radish seeds

1 tbsp sunflower seeds

❯ First prepare the soaked and sprouted ingredients in advance. Then chop all the vegetables and herbs as suggested and place them in a bowl. Add the soaked and sprouted items, toss gently and sprinkle with the soaked black sesame seeds and edible flowers for enrichment.

Nutrition Facts: Did you know that when you sprout sunflowers seeds, you'll give your bird a nutritious seed? Sprouted sunflower seeds contain high levels of B vitamins, especially folic acid, which is linked to healthy brain development. They are also rich in minerals, especially zinc and protein.

Garden Chop

Vegetables and Herbs

¼ cup cucumber, thinly sliced

¼ cup courgette (zucchini), thinly sliced

¼ cup white cabbage, chopped

1 carrot, peeled, grated

½ green bell pepper, chopped

1 tbsp fresh parsley, finely chopped

Handful of coriander microgreens

1 Scotch bonnet chilli pepper, thick sliced, to garnish

¼ small beetroot, cut into strips, to garnish

Viola (edible flowers), to garnish

Dry Items

1 tbsp shelled hemp seeds

1 tbsp organic rolled oats (unsweetened)

1 tbsp Polly's avian herbal tea

Soaked

1 tbsp red lentils

1 tbsp rye grain

1 tbsp pecan nuts, chopped

Sprouted

1 tbsp red quinoa

1 tbsp chickpeas (garbanzo beans)

1 tbsp barley grain

❯ Prepare the soaked and sprouted ingredients in advance. Chop all the vegetables and herbs as suggested and place them in a bowl. Add the dry, soaked and sprouted ingredients, toss gently and garnish with the chilli pepper, beetroot and edible flowers. This meal can also be served on a parrot-safe plate to encourage foraging.

Birdie's Mash

Vegetables and Herbs

1 broccoli floret

½ cup fresh dandelion leaves

¼ cup cauliflower

¼ cup white chicory

4 green beans, chopped

1 thin slice of raw sweet potato, grated

1 tbsp coriander microgreens

1 sprig of fresh coriander

1 sprig of fresh rosemary, to garnish

1 tbsp borage (edible flowers), to garnish

1 tbsp pomegranate seeds

Dry Items

1 tbsp hemp seeds

1 tbsp pumpkin seeds (pepitas)

1 tsp flaxseeds (linseeds)

Soaked

1 tbsp black sesame seeds

1 tbsp hulled millet

1 tbsp red lentils

> First prepare the soaked ingredients in advance. As this recipe is for smaller beaks use the food processor to chop the vegetables and herbs (except the green beans, sweet potato and microgreens) until finely chopped and mix them in a bowl. Add the dry and soaked ingredients, green beans, grated sweet potato, microgreens and the pomegranate seeds, and toss gently. Garnish with the edible flowers and a sprig of rosemary.

Savoy Salad

Vegetables and Herbs
½ cup savoy cabbage, chopped
½ yellow bell pepper, chopped
4 Brussels sprouts, quartered
¼ turnip, diced
½ cup red chicory, thinly sliced
½ cup purple broccoli, chopped
½ cup courgette, thick slices cut in half
1 sprig of fresh dill, chopped
1 tbsp fresh sage, finely chopped
Viola or Tagetes (edible flowers), to garnish

Dry Items
1 tbsp macadamia nuts, roughly chopped
1 tbsp natural sesame seeds
1 spray millet, chopped, to garnish

Soaked
1 tbsp hulled millet
1 tbsp milk thistle seeds

> First prepare the soaked ingredients in advance. Chop all the vegetables and herbs as suggested and place them in a bowl. Add the dry and soaked ingredients (except the spray millet), toss gently and garnish with the edible flowers and chopped spray millet. This meal is suitable for larger beaks.

Pea Shoots Chop

Vegetables and Herbs
Handful of pea shoots
¼ cup cucumber, chopped
¼ cup pak choi (bok choy), sliced
1 small carrot, thinly sliced
½ bell pepper, sliced
4 Brussels sprouts, finely chopped
¼ cup butternut squash, diced
Handful of baby spinach, chopped
2 sprigs of fresh sage, finely chopped
1 butternut squash, sliced and cut into star shape, to garnish

Soaked
1 tbsp black quinoa
1 tbsp natural sesame seeds

Sprouted
1 tbsp adzuki beans
1 tbsp mung beans
1 tbsp spelt grain

> First prepare the soaked and sprouted ingredients in advance. Place the pea shoots at the bottom of your bird's bowl. Chop all the other vegetables and herbs as suggested, then add all the soaked and sprouted ingredients and mix everything together. Place the mix onto the pea shoots and garnish with a butternut squash star.

Budgie Mash

Vegetables and Herbs

2 tbsp courgette
(zucchini)
¼ yellow bell pepper
2 tbsp turnip
1 radish
1 tbsp spinach
½ carrot
1 floret purple broccoli
1 tbsp pea shoots,
chopped
1 tbsp raw sweetcorn
(not from a tin)
1 tbsp basil
1 sprig of fresh dill
1 Scotch bonnet chilli
pepper, to garnish
1 slice of ripe yellow
plantain, lightly
steamed, to garnish

1 tsp hemp oil

Dry Items

1 tsp barley flakes
1 tsp flaxseeds
(linseeds)

Soaked

1 tsp sunflower seeds
1 tsp teff
1 tsp amaranth
1 tsp pecan nuts,
chopped, to garnish

Sprouted

1 tsp broccoli seeds
1 tsp spelt grain
1 tsp red clover seeds

> First prepare the soaked and sprouted ingredients in advance. Using a food processor, process the vegetables and herbs (except the pea shoots and sweetcorn) until finely chopped. Add the dry, soaked and sprouted ingredients as well as the teaspoon of hemp oil. Mix well. Place the mixture in a bowl and garnish with the slice of plantain, the Scotch bonnet chilli pepper and the chopped pecan nuts.

FRUIT SALADS

Fruit is a great source of fibre, a whole host of vitamins, antioxidants and other nutrients but it should not be the predominant part of your bird's diet.

Papaya Fruit Bowl

¼ cup papaya (including seeds), diced
½ kiwi, diced
2 tbsp pomegranate seeds

Dry Items
1 tsp chia seeds
1 tsp barley flakes
1 tbsp organic edible rose petals, to garnish

Soaked
1 tbsp almonds, to garnish

> Soak the almonds a day before making the salad. Chop the papaya and kiwi, add the pomegranate seeds followed by the dry items and mix well. Garnish with the almonds and rose petals. Leave the fruit bowl aside for about 5 minutes so the chia seeds can absorb the moisture from the fruit.

Tip: *Rose petals are great source of vitamin C, rich in antioxidants that help to cleanse the body from the effects of free radicals. Great for species that are iron sensitive. Rose petals can be mixed in your bird's fresh food or offered as a tea.*

Parrot's Fine Fruit Platter

1 slice of Santa Claus melon, for the bottom base, keep the flesh

½ yellow plantain, raw, sliced (must be ripe otherwise must be lightly steamed)

½ carrot, grated

¼ cup papaya, including the seeds, diced

1 tbsp organic blueberries, whole

¼ cup strawberries, chopped

Nasturtium and cornflowers (edible flowers), to garnish

> Cut off a thick slice from the melon approximately 1 cm thick, take out the flesh and put it aside. Slice the plantain and put it aside. Chop the other ingredients as instructed except the blueberries and place them in a bowl. Then add the flesh from the melon and mix everything well. Put the melon base onto a plate or in a bowl and start placing the plantain slices on top close to the edge and work your way around. With a spoon, put the fruit mix on top. Garnish with the edible flowers.

Polly's Muesli Bowl

½ red apple, chopped

1 small carrot, grated

¼ cup Santa Claus melon, including the seeds, diced

2 tbsp papaya, including the seeds, diced

¼ cup yellow plantain, lightly steamed, sliced, to garnish

1 sprig of fresh mint, to garnish

1 cornflower (edible flower), to garnish

Dry Items

1 tbsp organic rolled oats (unsweetened)

1 tbsp Brazil nuts, finely chopped

½ Ceylon cinnamon stick, crushed

Soaked

1 tbsp buckwheat

> Chop the carrot and all the fruit as instructed and place them in a bowl. Then add the dry and soaked ingredients and mix everything together gently. Garnish with the sliced plantain and cornflower, or just fresh mint.

Cherry Fruit Tower

5 cherries – cut in halves (pit must be removed)

¼ orange, chopped (feed sparingly)

½ red apple, peeled, chopped

2 strawberries, sliced

½ nectarine (remove pit), sliced

¼ carrot, grated

Dry Items

1 tbsp pecan nuts

1 tsp hazelnuts, chopped

1 tsp barley flakes

1 tbsp of a dried fruit mix – hawthorn berries, juniper berries, elderberries, rosehips, mountain ash berries (rowan berries), blueberries (optional)

› Chop the fruit and carrot as instructed and mix them with the dry items. Put the mixture in your bird's bowl and garnish with extra slices of orange and apple. Complete this dish by placing a cherry on top.

Mango – Quinoa Bowl

2 tbsp mango, ripe, diced

½ red apple, diced

½ small carrot, grated

1 tbsp pomegranate seeds

4 larger strawberries, sliced

2 sprigs of fresh mint, 1 finely chopped, 1 to garnish

1 tsp raw coconut oil

Dry Items

1 tbsp rosehips

2 tbsp rolled oats (unsweetened)

1 tbsp walnuts and cashews, whole or chopped

1 tbsp coconut flakes (unsweetened), to garnish

Soaked

1 tbsp red quinoa

› First soak the quinoa for about 4 hours in cool water prior to making this meal. Once soaked, rinse well and let it drain. Place the strawberry slices around the bowl.

› Chop the remaining fruit as instructed and mix it together with the soaked quinoa, dry items, fresh mint and coconut oil. Place the fruit mix in the middle of the bed of strawberry slices. Garnish with the coconut flakes and the sprig of mint.

Fruity Mix

¼ papaya, including seeds
1 nectarine, chopped
¼ red organic apple, seedless
1 tbsp orange, chopped
1 tbsp grapes, cut in half
1 cup watermelon, diced
1 tbsp banana "chips", thinly sliced

1 sprig of fresh mint, chopped

Dry Items
1 tbsp shelled hemp seeds
2 tsp chia seeds

Soaked
1 tbsp almonds

> First soak the almonds a day before making this meal. Chop all the fruit and mint as suggested, set the papaya aside, and place the rest of the fruit and the mint in a bowl. Add the soaked almonds and the dry items, mix well and place the quarter papaya on top so your bird can forage first on the papaya seeds.

Dragon Fruit Bowl

½ dragon fruit, peeled, chopped
1 tbsp strawberries, chopped
1 tbsp blueberries
1 tbsp blackberries
½ kiwi, chopped
1 tbsp pomegranate seeds
1 sprig of fresh mint, chopped
1 fresh fig, chopped
1 slice of fresh fig, to garnish

1 slice of dragon fruit, to garnish
Cornflower and pansies (edible flowers), to garnish

Dry Items
1 tsp chia seeds
1 tbsp almonds
1 tbsp coconut flakes (unsweetened)

> Chop all the fruit as instructed, place it in a bowl and mix with the dry items. Garnish with the slice of dragon fruit and fig by placing them on top of the mix. Finish it off with some edible flowers for enrichment.

Carrot-Mango Muesli Bowl

1 tbsp mango, chopped
½ red apple, grated
½ peach, finely
  chopped
½ carrot, grated
Watermelon, to garnish

Dry Items
1 tsp chia seeds
1 tbsp rolled oats
  (unsweetened)
1 tbsp hemp seeds
Star anise, to garnish

❯ Chop the carrot and all the fruit as instructed and place them in a bowl. Add the dry ingredients and mix everything together gently. Garnish with a small slice of watermelon and star anise. Get creative and use cookie cutters of various shapes to cut out different fruit shapes for the garnish.

Melon Marbles

1 watermelon	**Dry Items**
1 Galia melon	1 tbsp coconut flour
1 dragon fruit	1 tbsp chia seeds
	1 tbsp shelled hemp seeds

〉 Cut both melons in half lengthwise. Scoop out the seeds from the Galia melon with a spoon and keep aside. Then take each half melon and begin to scoop with a melon baller by pressing the tool down into the flesh of the fruit; then rotate it to form a ball-shaped piece. Transfer the melon balls to a bowl and repeat. Try to scoop the fruit as close together as possible so there is minimum wastage. Do the same with the dragon fruit.
〉 To make the balls even more fun for your bird you can roll some of them in one of the dry ingredients. Simply place the coconut flour, chia seeds and hemp seeds on separate plates and roll some of the balls across the plate. Have fun with your bird.

Tip: Seeds from both melons are perfectly safe for your parrot to eat and you can simply allow your parrot to pick them directly from the fruit.

Exotic Fruit Mix

1 tbsp blueberries	1 sprig of fresh mint, to garnish
1 tbsp blackberries	
½ peach, chopped	**Dry Items**
½ cup watermelon, diced	1 tbsp coconut flakes (unsweetened)
1 tbsp grapes, cut in halves	Star anise, to garnish
½ kiwi, chopped	**Soaked**
1 tbsp strawberries, chopped	1 tbsp red quinoa
2 sprigs of redcurrants, to garnish	

〉 Chop all the fruit as instructed and place it in a bowl. Add the dry items and the soaked quinoa, and mix gently. Garnish with couple of sprigs of redcurrant, fresh mint and star anise.

Star Fruit Messy Platter

½ kiwi, sliced

1 fresh fig, quartered

½ star fruit, ripe, peeled, chopped

1 tbsp strawberries, chopped

1 tbs grapes, cut in halves

½ pear, chopped

½ peach, chopped

1 tbsp blueberries

1 passion fruit

1 sprig of fresh mint, finely chopped

1 tsp raw coconut oil

Pansies (edible flowers), to garnish

Dry Items

1 tsp chia seeds

1 tbsp rolled oats (unsweetened)

1 tbsp rosehips

1 tbsp almonds, chopped

❯ First chop the star fruit, strawberries, grapes, pear, peach and fresh mint as instructed and place them in a bowl. Add the whole blueberries. Cut the passion fruit in half and with a spoon remove the pulp from the rind. Place the pulp into the fruit mix, together with the coconut oil and all the dry ingredients. Mix well. Take the sliced kiwi and place it around the plate leaving space in the middle for the fruit mix. Using a spoon, transfer the fruit mix onto the plate and place it in the middle. To make it more fun, use cookie cutters of various shapes to cut out some pieces from the pear and the star fruit, and place on top as desired. Cut the fresh fig into quarters and just place them around the edge of the plate. Edible flowers will always make it an even more delicious-looking meal.

FORAGING TREATS

Foraging is essential part of your bird's life, hence including food items or foraging toys that can trigger this natural behaviour is crucial to stimulate their minds and make them work for their food.

Banana Split

½ yellow plantain, must be ripe or lightly steamed
½ carrot, sliced
¼ beetroot, sliced
1 baby sweetcorn, sliced
1 leaf rainbow chard

1 chilli pepper, to garnish

Dry Items
1 tsp hemp seeds
1 tsp white hulled sesame seeds

> First peel and split the plantain in half lengthways and place it on the rainbow chard leaf. Cut the other vegetables as suggested and simply top the plantain with them as you like. Get creative. Cut the end of the chilli pepper and put it on one end of the plantain. Sprinkle with hemp and sesame seeds to make a fun meal for your bird.

Tip: Plantains are often confused with bananas, but they offer much more. It is known that plantains help to boost the immune system and are high in fibre which helps to regulate the digestive system; they are rich in potassium that helps maintain the skeleton system and muscles, and plays a major role in regulating blood pressure; they are also high in vitamins A and C, and contain less sugar than bananas. There are two types of plantains: yellow and green. Green tastes a bit like potato when cooked and yellow has a sweeter taste. When offering plantains to your pet bird make sure the green plantain is always cooked/steamed, and the yellow must be ripe if offered raw.

Hanging Kabobs

Vegetable Kabob
Pak choi (bok choy)
Radish
Swede (rutabaga)
Brussels sprouts
Sweet potato
Butternut squash
Cucumber
Beetroot
Green pepper

Fruit Kabob
Galia melon
Apple
Dragon fruit
Blueberries
Strawberry
Pansy edible flowers

❯ Hanging skewers are super easy to make and will offer your bird mental stimulation as well as food. It is great to use this method when introducing a new vegetable or fruit. Always use a parrot-safe stainless-steel skewer and thread a selection of the suggested vegetables and fruit onto each skewer. You can always substitute for any vegetable or fruit that you have available or you can mix a few vegetables on a fruit skewer or vice versa. Fruit and vegetables can be cut into smaller pieces or threaded on the skewer whole. This is suitable for all beaks.

"Takeaway" Parrot Chop

1 small carrot
5 green beans
¼ cup orange bell
  pepper
2 whole radishes
¼ cup courgette
  (zucchini)
½ beetroot, diced
¼ cup sugar snap peas
1 sprig fresh coriander,
  finely chopped
1 sprig of fresh
  rosemary, to garnish

Dry Items
1 tbsp walnuts, crushed
1 tsp Polly's avian
  herbal tea

Soaked
1 tbsp yellow split peas
1 tbsp green and brown
  lentils
1 tbsp white quinoa

Sprouted
1 tbsp mung beans
1 tbsp barley grain
1 tbsp broccoli seeds

1 bamboo food-grade
  cone – your bird will
  love shredding it

〉 Chop up all the vegetables and herbs and place them in a bowl. Mix in the dry, soaked and sprouted items. With a spoon, fill up the bamboo cone and place it either on a plate to avoid the mess or in your bird's bowl. Now the shredding can begin.

Sweet Potato – Courgette Foraging Platter

¼ sweet potato, sliced,
  lightly steamed
3 slices of courgette
  (zucchini)
2 okras
1 tbsp chard
  microgreens
5 raw whole peas

½ white chicory, sliced
Pansies (edible
  flowers), to garnish

Soaked
1 tbsp walnuts
1 bamboo skewer

〉 First cut the sweet potato into three slices and place them into a steamer basket and cover. Steam for about 3 minutes, remove and let it cool. Take the bamboo skewer and thread the vegetables listed above, starting with a slice of courgette then sweet potato and finishing with a slice of okra. Place the chard microgreens in between the courgette and the sweet potato. Put the skewer on a plate and garnish it with sliced chicory, whole peas, chopped okra, soaked walnuts and edible flowers.

Courgette Cactus

½ courgette (zucchini)   Food-grade paper
1 carrot, peeled   Paper rope
Brazil nuts

> With a knife, remove the top of the courgette to create a stable platform. You will need to hollow out one end of the courgette to create a cup-like holder for the carrot chips. To do this, take a teaspoon or special corer and carefully insert it about 3 cm into the courgette. Twist and pull out the courgette flesh. Then use the corer to make a few holes in the courgette below the hollow part. Cut the peeled carrot into thin chips.
> Cut out a square shape of the food-grade paper and wrap the paper around the base of the courgette with the hollow part upwards. Secure it with a paper rope at the bottom, making sure the courgette will stand upright. Then start inserting Brazil nuts into the holes around the courgette and place the carrot chips inside the hollow part.

Artichoke Bouquet

1 large artichoke   courgette (zucchini)
butternut squash   fennel
carrot   radish
beetroot   sugar snap peas
butternut squash   fresh oregano
cauliflower   1 tsp Polly's avian
broccoli   herbal tea, to garnish
chillies

> Rinse the artichoke well, tugging the leaves outward to loosen slightly so they are ready for stuffing. Cut the bottom part of the butternut squash and scoop out the flesh. This will be used as a base. Then place the artichoke inside.
> Cut all the vegetables into long chunky strips and stuff under each leaf, starting from the bottom and working your way around. To finish it off sprinkle with the avian herbal tea.

ABOUT THE AUTHOR

Karmen Budai

Karmen Budai started off with her successful book, *A Parrot's Fine Cuisine Cookbook and Nutritional Guide*, published in 2018. Her parrot's story was the main factor that prompted her to create her first cookbook for parrot owners and set her on the journey of helping other parrot owners struggling to feed their birds a healthy nutritional diet.

Her passion for parrots and their wellbeing then led her to the creation of her second book, *A Healthy Parrot's Meal Planner*, to inspire other bird owners and help them on their journey with their bird diet transition. She has dedicated a significant amount of her time researching and educating herself about avian nutrition from the best and fully qualified experts in the avian field.

Karmen is originally from a small country in Europe called Slovakia. Since childhood, she had a creative streak, which led to studying fashion design in her college years. Fashion remained a hobby and she moved on to a career in the corporate environment.

She moved to the United Kingdom in 2004, intending only to stay for a few years, but settled there with her family. She has the most demanding, feathered, velcro cockatoo, called Polly, that consumes the majority of the family's time. Polly is a toddler that will never grow up. There are also new additions to the family: three delightful budgies and an Indian Ringneck Parakeet, Rio, who's the family's little chatterbox.

Karmen Budai now runs her own online store for avian herbal tea provisions, first in the UK and Europe, called Polly's Natural Parrot Boutique, which is another way of helping to provide enrichment to all birds and goes hand in hand with the message she's eager to share with all parrot owners.

ABOUT THE CONTRIBUTORS

Dr Karen Shaw Becker

Karen Shaw Becker received her degree in veterinary medicine from the Iowa State School of Veterinary Medicine. Dr Becker completed exotic animal internships in California and at the Berlin Zoo, Germany, and is certified in acupuncture, homeopathy and rehabilitation. Dr Becker is the founder of Natural Pet Animal Hospital, Feathers Bird Clinic and TheraPaw Rehabilitation and Pain Management Clinic in Illinois. She is also licensed by the US Fish and Wildlife Service to rehabilitate injured and orphaned endangered species through her non-profit organization, Covenant Wildlife. Dr Becker often lectures and writes about species-appropriate nutrition and has co-authored the Whole Dog Journal's Best Homemade Diet Book of All Time award, *Real Food for Healthy Pets*. She was deeply honoured to be named one of Chicago's Top Ten Vets, according to *Chicago Magazine*, and is the most followed veterinarian in the world, according to Facebook. Dr Becker is also the veterinary consultant for Mercola Healthy Pets, the largest pet wellness website on the internet. She consults for a variety of pet wellness and pet food companies, designing diets and pet health products to improve the wellbeing of companion animals worldwide.

Dr Stephanie Lamb

Stephanie Lamb, DVM, Dipl ABVP, has always desired to provide good health, happiness and care to all animals. She grew up in Las Vegas, NV, and after graduating from UNLV with a BS in Biology, she attended veterinary school at the University of Minnesota. Upon finishing veterinary school she performed a one-year internship in avian and exotic medicine followed by a two-year residency in avian medicine and surgery in Wilton, CT. After completing her residency, Dr Lamb worked in Southern California and Arizona at exotics-exclusive animal hospitals. During this time she gained extensive knowledge and became skilled in treating exotic mammals, birds, reptiles, amphibians and wildlife. During her career she has also worked with many humane societies, parrot and rabbit rescue groups, wildlife centres and raptor rehabilitation facilities. She is always striving to learn more and is focused on contributing to the advancement of knowledge of avian and exotic animal medicine by providing the highest quality veterinary care possible. She and her husband share their home with dogs, geckos, fish, and 13 birds. Dr Lamb passed her Avian Medicine boards in the autumn of 2014. She has publications in peer-reviewed journals about avian and exotic mammal medicine and has lectured at county, state and national veterinary conferences about avian medicine. She has also spoken to local bird, reptile and rabbit clubs in her community.

Dr Jamie Abete

 Jamie Abete, DVM, has always had a passion for caring for animals. She grew up in the suburbs of Chicago surrounded by a variety of animal companions. She has raised parrots for over two decades as well as some soft bill and toucan species. She completed her Bachelor's degree in Biology at Benedictine University in Lisle, Illinois and later studied biology with an emphasis on Zoo and Aquarium Studies through Western Illinois University.

During veterinary school at Ross University School of Veterinary Medicine she was actively involved in wildlife rehabilitation through Ross University's student chapter of AAV (Association of Avian Veterinarians) and feral cat population management via the university's TNR (trap neuter and release) programme. She also was involved in research in the Microbiology Department studying various tick-borne diseases and the prevalence of infection and co-infections in the canine population on the island of St Kitts, West Indies, which was later published in PLOS One.

Since graduation from veterinary school Dr Abete has worked at Niles Animal Hospital and Bird Medical Center which was founded in 1949 by Dr Lafeber who was one of the leading minds in pet bird care and nutrition. She currently is the veterinarian for multiple parrot rescues in the Chicago area as well as several nature centres treating un-releasable ambassador animals including coyotes, owls, hawks, vultures, turtles and salamanders. Dr Abete has a special interest in wildlife and behavioural medicine. She is also certified in Low Stress Handling.

Outside of practising medicine, Dr Abete has a certificate in hatha yoga instruction and enjoys regularly practising yoga. Her other hobbies include animal training, bird watching, gardening, photography and painting. She shares her home with her husband as well as her multiple birds, geckos, cats and dog.

RESOURCES

Avian Herbal Teas

Unique avian herbal tea provisions in the UK and Europe. We believe that by including avian herbal teas in your bird's diet you can enhance their quality of life.
www.pollysnaturalparrotboutique.com
Facebook: @pollysnaturalparrotboutique
Instagram: @pollysnaturalparrotboutique
Twitter: @pollysnaturalp1

Follow Polly on Parrot's Fine Cuisine for more parrot recipes and avian nutrition
Facebook: @parrotsfinecuisinecookbook
Instagram: @parrotsfinecuisinecookbook
Twitter: @parrotsfine

Please think about donating a small amount to support these great charities who are trying to improve lives of so many parrots.

World Parrot Trust
An international leader in science-based, results-oriented, parrot conservation and welfare efforts since 1989
www.parrots.org
Facebook: @WorldParrotTrust
Twitter: @ParrotTrust

Australia

Queenslander Aviaries
Gourmet Seed Blends, Pellets, Sprouts, Supplements, Toys and Accessories.
www.queenslanderaviaries.com
Facebook: @queenslanderaviaries
Instagram: @queenslanderaviaries

Happy Wings Sanctuary
Happy Wings Sanctuary is a 501(c)3 non-profit sanctuary whose mission is to help educate, rehabilitate, and transform the lives of unwanted and neglected parrots.
www.happywingssanctuary.com
Facebook: @HappyWingsSanctuary
Instagram: @HappyWingsSanctuary

US

True Leaf Market

High Quality, Affordable Seeds, Delivered Fast.
www.trueleafmarket.com
Facebook: @trueleafmarket
Twitter: @trueleafmarket
Instagram: @trueleafmarket
www.youtube.com/trueleafmarket
www.pinterest.com/trueleafmarket

Parrot Magazine

UK

ExoticDirect

Insurance for large and small birds as well as other exotic pets. Winners of the Feefo Gold Trusted Service Award 2020.
www.exoticdirect.co.uk
Facebook: @ExoticDirect pet insurance
Twitter: @ExoticDirect
Instagram: @exoticdirect

Parrot insurance

Dr Stephanie Lamb, DVM, Dipl ABVP (Avian Practice)
www.azeah.com

Please join us at **www.pollysnaturalparrotboutique.com** to receive updates, giveaways and notifications of new products.

If you would like to know more about advertising in Polly's editions, please contact us at **info@pollysnaturalparrotboutique.com**

TICK TOCK

It's parrot tea time...

ORGANIC AVIAN HERBAL TEA

Formulated by US biologist and nutrition consultant Dr J.Crean

Delight your bird's senses with our unique avian herbal blends. Refreshing, nutritional and made with love for your bird.

NATURE BOOST

Supporting a healthy immune system naturally

ETERNAL FEATHERS

Not only good for the body but also the mind of your pet bird. Great for skin and feathers.

GOLDDEN BLOSSOM

This tea blend is meant to support the natural cleanse processes that take place in the body.

www.pollysnaturalparrotboutique.com